WHAT THE ANCIENTS SAID

Books by Lou D'Angelo

WHAT THE ANCIENTS SAID
HOW TO BE AN ITALIAN

WHAT THE ANCIENTS SAID

LOU D'ANGELO

DOUBLEDAY & COMPANY, INC.
GARDEN CITY, NEW YORK
1971

First Edition

Library of Congress Catalog Card Number 71–139012
Copyright © 1971 by Lou D'Angelo
All Rights Reserved
Printed in the United States of America

To Iya

WHAT THE ANCIENTS SAID

THE ANCIENTS

My brother Vinnie and I were brought up on Sicilian proverbs, most of them enigmatic. I will admit some made more sense than others. One time, after it had become apparent that I wasn't going to grow to a very imposing height, my father reassured me by quoting the old Sicilian proverb, *The short tree bears good fruit; cut the tall tree at the roots.* My brother, who was ten years older and a foot taller than I, betrayed apprehension at this, so my mother thought to calm him with another proverb, *The tall one for his presence, the short one for his wisdom.* It was my grandfather who prevented Vinnie from dissolving into tears. He complimented him with a third Sicilian proverb, *The hairy man is fortunate.* At the time, my brother was already shaving every other day.

But a more typical saying went, *King Solomon, for all his sapience, died without assistance.* I gave a good deal of thought to that one. I came closest to penetrating its mystery on a summer night when Vinnie was sitting with my grandfather on the fire escape. The sound of the old man's singing reached me at the kitchen table where I had

9

stopped trying to puzzle out proverbs for a crack at the equally awesome problems of long division.

The dimensions of that table were imposing, even by kitchen standards of thirty years ago. At its other end, my mother sat helping my grandmother with *her* homework. As on most nights, there were half a dozen or so cutaway coats, soon destined for the showrooms of what my grandmother called *Li Roggispiti*, resting in amorphous black lumps where, an hour earlier, there had been plates heaped with macaroni. While my mother removed long white stitches from around the armholes of a coat draped over her knees, my grandmother sewed short black stitches into the interior of another, which she carefully coaxed along her lap. My mother worked in silence, pausing only to push back her eyeglasses and give me loving glances. My grandmother chattered incessantly about the buttonhole maker, the presser, and *La Fineeshi*, her co-workers at *Li Roggispiti*. (It didn't take much imagination to deduce that *La Fineeshi's* job involved putting finishing touches on the cutaways, but it wasn't until years later, when I walked by a Rogers Peet clothing store, that I realized where my grandmother's homework assignments had come from.)

When I identified what my grandfather was singing, I shoved my notebook toward the table's garment district, and stepped out the kitchen window to join the men.

"So the King Solomon proverb is really a song," I said to my grandfather in Sicilian dialect. He stopped singing and puffed at his pipe, staring out from under his cap at our neighbor's back yard, where the fig tree grew.

"What does it mean?" I asked.

He sighed, looked up at the moon, and supplicated, *"Beautiful moon, full moon, my house always filled with wheat and flour, save me from bad neighbors."*

Neighbors were frequently mentioned in Sicilian proverbs. The pithiest one declared that all of them were werewolves. Another said, *The neighbor is a serpent; if she doesn't see you, she'll hear you.*

My grandfather was probably jealous of his neighbor's fig tree, the focal point of a beautifully kept garden transversed by paved walks, and an incongruous oasis among the grubby rears of those East Harlem tenements. He had only a few flowerpots on the fire escape in which to foster his agricultural heritage. He did a good job with what was available. Every year he harvested a bumper crop of mint, parsley, and sweet basil for our macaroni, and complaints from our landlord, Filippo.

Filippo lived in fear of the day our fire escape would be inspected by the New York City Fire Department. As far as I know, it never was. Even had my grandfather voluntarily removed all his pots, I don't know how we could have escaped a fire by that route anyway. There was no opening in the fire escape, and no ladder.

"Sing the King Solomon song again," I said, to get my grandfather back on the subject.

He began in an assured baritone, "And King Solomon, for all his sapience, died without assistance, and with a spoon in his ass."

I was grateful for this additional clue to the sapient one's demise, but they were the only words my grandfather sang. He hummed the rest of the melody in a tremulous diminuendo.

"Isn't there more to it?"

"There is, but I've forgotten the words."

"What is the meaning?" I persisted.

"The meaning is that King Solomon was a very wise man of whom many people, including, and especially, his sister, were jealous. And for all his majestic learning, he died without help, with a spoon stuck in his ass. The ancients said, *Things there are, but we are not obliged to believe them.*"

My grandfather had ended his explanation with the most quoted Sicilian proverb of all. What the ancients probably had in mind was authenticating Sicilian beliefs in witchcraft, ghosts, and evil omens, while noting their lack of ecclesiastical approbation. In our corner of the new world, this pronouncement served as an all-purpose comment on everything from small pleasures to major catastrophes. My grandmother, particularly, repeated it several times a day.

In contrast, there was another proverb that was used exceedingly sparingly—only when there was a rainbow visible in the sky over East Harlem. Two or three times while I was growing up, my grandmother intoned it, *Noah's Ark: There is still some world left.*

Like my grandmother, each member of our household had a favorite aphorism. My hairy brother's, of course, had been provided by my grandfather, whose own favorite was, *Raise high the foot, for I touch straw.* From my grandmother I learned that this had to do with laziness. The reference was to running away from honest work in the hayloft. I guess it was my favorite, too.

My mother observed that *Things there are . . .* nearly as frequently as her mother did, but even more often she said, *All evil does not come to harm.* I succeeded in peeling away the literal translation to discover that every cloud has a silver lining.

When my father, who was five feet, four inches tall, inspiringly compared the relative worth of short and tall trees, he was quoting his own favorite proverb. Actually, this was the only one I ever heard him use, and he did so infrequently. My father liked this country and its customs, and often showed impatience with the way my mother and her side of the family clung to the old ways. He always spoke to my brother and me in English, which, because he had lived for a few years in New Orleans, was in the accents of both southern Italy and southern United States. We rarely had anything to say to him in return.

My mother and my grandparents spoke almost no English but had molded a few English words into Sicilian. At least one other emigrant from their home town of Camporeale had done the same. He was Mase Miale, to whom was attributed a lengthy series of quasi-proverbs based on puns and intended to show the futility of life in America. The story had it that after Mase had been in New York for three months, he urinated into New York harbor and took the next ship home. Typical of Mase Miale's comments were: "What a country! Broad avenues that take half a day to cross they call *stritti*. Pink cheeked, healthy babies are named *gianni*. Lads of good family they call *boia*. Who can live in such a country?" The legendary Mase's less-than-perfect pronunciation had turned "street," "Johnny," and "boy," into homophones for the Sicilian-dialect words meaning, respectively, "narrow," "yellow," and "hangman."

Another Camporealese, Michelune, had coined a proverb which I never heard spoken without attribution, probably because it rhymed that way. *Michelune lassa dittu: Cu fa bene e maledittu* [Michelune left it said: Who does good is damned].

Except for the canon of Mase Miale, and Michelune's stunning dictum, proverbs were usually credited to "the ancients." The ancients had their biggest moment in East Harlem at three o'clock one morning, a few minutes after an attempted robbery. A noise in the kitchen had awakened my grandfather, who grabbed the wood-chopping hatchet he kept under his cot, leaped from under the covers, and chased a shadowy figure out the window. When my grandfather, nightshirt flying, bounded onto the fire escape, ready to chop the would-be malefactor down to size, he found no one there. Terrible in his frustrated wrath, he proceeded to wake up everybody with some of the most bloodcurdling yells heard since the Sicilian Vespers. My mother, herself trembling, told me not to be frightened. My grandmother, a sound sleeper who did not awaken graciously under any circumstances, cast doubt on my grandfather's story. "The ancients said, *The wise man schemes, the lazy man dreams.* You had a nightmare."

My offended grandfather came back at her. "The ancients said, *Beware of the marked woman.*" (My grandmother had a small mole at the back of her neck.) "They also said, *Head that sleeps more than three hours, step on it.*"

"*The hunchback sees other's infirmities, but not his own,*" my grandmother shot back.

"The ancients were right, *The bad year may be late in coming, but it always comes.*"

"*He who sits uncomfortably thinks evil thoughts,*" said my grandmother, in a masterpiece of Sicilian relevancy.

"*The nagging wife is a cross for life,*" my grandfather answered.

"Not necessarily in this country," my father broke in.

At this critical point, I extricated myself from my mother's protective embrace to come to my grandfather's defense. I had heard the commotion that preceeded his bawling reveille, I said. My grandmother fixed me with a betrayed look. It made me think she was going to quote Michelune at me. Instead, she asked how any burglar could disappear on a fire escape such as ours.

"*Things there are, but we are not obliged to believe them,*" I said. She nodded thoughtfully, or maybe just sleepily, and went back to bed.

THE NAMES

Of my brother's name there was no doubt. Vinnie's birth certificate read Vincenzo Martana. Of my own name, Gaetano Martana on the birth certificate, there was no certainty. Probably because "Tano" is short for Gaetano, someone in our family, I don't know who, thought my given name translated into English as Thomas. Thus, at home I was called Tommy, while in convivial moments at school some of my Italo-American classmates referred to me as Tommaso.

"It's Gaetano," I'd explain.

"But your name is Tommy. That's Tommaso, ain't it?"

"It's also Gaetano," I'd assure them, not at all sure of it myself.

Both my brother's name and mine had been mandated before we were born. The Sicilian tradition was that a first-born son had to be named after his paternal grandfather; a first-born daughter after her paternal grandmother; second sons and second daughters after the maternal grandparents. Subsequent issue honored the grandparents' siblings, in chronological order. Only Sicilian parents of

16

prodigious fecundity ever went outside the family for names.

So my father, the eldest of ten children in his family, was named Mario after his father's father. My mother, eldest of nine children, only four of whom survived infancy, was named after her father's mother, Santina. Her brothers, Nick and Charlie Tarantola, baptized Tarantola Nicola and Calogero (the latter occasioning another doubtful translation), and her sister Pina, who was two months younger than my brother, were all named for the appropriate relatives.

These rules were at least as important in our family as the Sacrament of Baptism itself. They allowed of no exception. They were so ingrained that even when Uncle Charlie broke the laws of the Church by marrying a non-Catholic in a civil ceremony, simultaneously exceeding the bounds of rational behavior because Barbara was also non-Sicilian and even non-Italian, he nevertheless followed the naming code. He called his first and only son Thomas, thereby perpetuating the Martana-Tarantola delusion that this was the American way of saying Gaetano. Since his wife, Barbara, the American, had wished the boy to be called Kenneth, of all things, he was given a middle name, something theretofore unknown in our family. My assertions that both my cousin and I had been victims of mistaken translation so confused my mother that she referred to Barbara and Charlie's child as Tommasu Kennu, though she would admit no error in my case.

That such store was set by given names seemed all the more puzzling when one considered how well endowed my progenitors, my grandmother in particular, were with the Sicilian talent for *la 'ngiuria* [the nickname]. For instance, in our building, according to my grandmother, lived a large widow called The Elephant, as well as The Dyed Redhead and her husband Suitcase Eyes, and Mr. and Mrs. Potato Nose. Their nicknames, like many Sicilian nicknames, were based on obvious physical characteristics. But also in the building lived the Lemon Peel family and La She-Bee. Nicknames could be acquired by the performance, within sight of the nicknamer, of an otherwise insignificant action —such as throwing lemon peels into a garbage can, or by saying something which struck the nicknamer as funny. La She-Bee, who spoke English, had once answered my grandmother's inquiry about the health of a hospitalized daughter by saying, "She'll be coming home soon."

Some nicknames were mysteriously abstract, like those my grandmother gave to our landlord's family. Filippo himself had none, possibly out of respect for his high station, but his wife was The Excommunicated Nun, and their children were The Old Nun, The Young Nun, and The Sexton. Other nicknames were spectacularly vulgar. A Camporealese who had been observed, half a century earlier, with a soggy trouser leg was still known by my grandfather as Nardo Piss-Backwards; our butcher was Turiddu Testicle Eyes; and an elderly Palermitan woman who had once worked with my grandmother at *Li Roggispiti* was *Vecchia Causi Fettusi* [Old Stink Pants]. This kind of nickname was usually a secret from the person nicknamed, but in my godfather's case I once may have given the game away.

My godfather, whose real name was Giuseppe Licari, was a noteworthy man in at least two respects. He had been Camporeale's leading intellectual, both by virtue of his academic attainments (he finished elementary school) and because he kept on reading after he graduated. Also, he had a reputation as a cheapskate. My grandparents never tired of telling me that Giuseppe and Martina Licari "should have been ashamed of themselves," because they'd renounced Satan for me at my christening, and then had given me one lousy dollar bill as a present.

Being both wealthy and smart, my godfather sang arias to himself, collected librettos, records, stamps, coins, tropical fish, etchings, books, and almost everything else most Sicilians regarded as worthless. During the first eight years of my life, when we lived in Newark, New Jersey, in the same apartment building as the Licaris, he also was an enthusiastic amateur photographer, mainly of me.

One sunny morning during my pre-kindergarten days, my godfather appeared at our door singing an Italian tune of the time, one line of which went: "*Addio Virginia, Vado in Abissinia* [Good-bye Virginia, I'm going to Abyssinia]." (There was another song on the same theme, *Faccetta Nera*, which forecast that soon every little black face would have a Roman nose.) He was carrying both of his cameras and a box. From the latter, he produced a red, white, and green sash which he wrapped over my shoulder and around my stomach, three medals, which made my shirt sag when he pinned them on, and an overseas cap which fit me perfectly, since my head was quite large for my age and size. So garbed, I was marched downstairs to the back yard and made to stand against the board fence. Still singing, my godfather extracted a final treasure from the box, a small Italian flag. He thrust it into my left hand, jerked my right hand upward, stepped back, snapped the picture, and ended his song on an enthusiastically martial note. In the developed photograph, my Fascist salute looked like a wave bye-bye.

One might think that such a man would be nicknamed for one of his eccentricities—The Skinflint Professor, perhaps, or Tropical Fish, or *Il Duce Fotografico*. Instead, though no part of his nose was ruddier than the rest of his face, he was known as Red Nostrils. He'd probably had a cold the day some forgotten nicknamer had had the muse upon him. But my godfather was one of the few people I ever heard about whose old nickname was eventually superseded by a new one. Only a momentous event could account for such a change, and it was my grandmother who somehow had witnessed this turning point in my godfather's life. By the time we were living in New York, her new nickname for Red Nostrils had become firmly established in our family. So it was that during a weekend when Mr. and Mrs. Licari paid us a visit, after my godfather had gone out to inspect the tropical fish markets of East Harlem, I inquired of my mother, within earshot of my godmother, "When is Overflowing Chamberpot coming back?"

The thought often occurred to me that if we had nicknames for nearly everyone we knew and even for many people whom we did not know, some of our *paisani* must have had nicknames for us. When I'd ask about it, my mother and grandmother would profess ignorance of any but their husbands' nicknames—The Standard Bearer and Carnival Face, respectively. My mother assured me that if I did have a nickname, it could only be one which honored my sweet disposition, such as "Pasta of Angels," or commented on my long eyelashes, "Fringed Loveliness." I can think of others that would have been more appropriate. Certainly Red Nostrils would have suited me better than it had my godfather, since I had to blow my nose many times a day even when I didn't have a cold. And my large skull suggested a descriptive nickname like Melon Head, which I'd heard applied to many people whose heads were no larger than mine. I could have been called Trembling Intestines or Unsevered Umbilicus or, because I didn't have anything to say when we had company, Rusted Tongue. A pair of nicknames my mother used for two different people on the block could have been combined easily to form one for me, Saint Sorrowful, the Hermit.

Despite my mother's unresponsiveness to my questions, I knew that she had a behind-his-back nickname for Vinnie: Fallen Arms. And she also had a second for my father.

My father's "official" nickname, The Standard Bearer, could be used to his face, despite its slightly patronizing tone. The phrase had originated in Sicily, with his mother.

Before my father, only two other Martanas, a pair of his uncles, had settled in America. Both died of influenza soon after they'd saved enough money to send for their wives. When a third Martana, my father's father, tried to go to New Orleans to look after the interests of his widowed sisters-in-law, he was turned back at Ellis Island. The old man, who was "full of pepper" and had such a violent temper that he was called Hot Sausage, to show his impatience at the questions of the immigration authorities, had rolled his eyes and hit his head against the wall. This was a routine Sicilian expression of annoyance, by no means unique with Hot Sausage. The functionaries at Ellis Island, unacquainted with this folkway, arranged my grandfather Martana's instant repatriation. It took many years for his ire to cool. But eventually their straitened circumstances made it imperative for a member of the clan to show the Martana flag in America again. My father, being the eldest son, was selected.

So that his two aunts would know what to expect, he was the subject of long descriptive letters prior to his arrival, written by his mother, *La Pirnacchia*. (This nickname, coined by the Tarantolas, meant, roughly, "big, ugly feather," and referred to a hat she'd once worn to church as a young woman.)

"How best to describe my magnificent son who, during the sixteen years of his life, has been the supreme glory of my existence?" she wrote. "Suffice it to say that he is the Standard Bearer for the town."

She meant that in the religious processions of Camporeale, it was my father who carried the heavy banner of Our Lady of the Sorrows.

His aunts must have confused strength with height, and were unprepared for the square little blacksmith's apprentice who arrived at the port of New Orleans. My father recalled that after some *paisani* he'd met on the boat had helped him convince them that he was indeed Mario

Martana, the two women took him home grudgingly, mumbling all the way about standard bearers. A day or two later they bought him a pair of knickers. After a few more days, he had been put to work in a sack factory, had his right leg broken when he was knocked down by a street car, and suffered minor burns by setting fire to his hospital bed while trying to sneak a smoke.

Despite this inauspicious beginning and the coolness of his welcome, he'd already begun to appreciate the American way of life, particularly the way of life of American girls.

So, when, shortly after his leg healed, someone told him that to please American girls he should have a simple operation performed, my father took a day off and returned to the hospital to be circumcized. He rested for just a few minutes, walked out, and hired a horse-drawn buggy to take him home. His aunts were sitting on their front porch when he came into view—an impressive sight in a new white suit and the fancy vehicle. The closer he came, the larger his aunts' eyes opened at the widening red stain in the crotch of his snowy pants. He greeted them, walked into the house, and collapsed.

I did not find my father's circumcision story particularly amusing, but he retold it regularly, usually at Uncle Charlie's request, to the accompaniment of raucous laughter. When it came to that part of his anatomy, I preferred hearing him reminisce about how, back in Camporeale, he had compared its size to that of his brother Vito's. Vito's precocious development had earned him the nickname of *Viscuttuni* [Big Biscuit]. My mother combined this nickname with the circumcision to form her secret nickname for my father. She used it more and more frequently in my presence as I grew older, usually in such sentences as, "Unhappiness is all I've ever had from Snipped Biscuit."

THE CURSE

The Martanas and the Tarantolas occupied the two top-floor apartments, three flights up, in Filippo's building. Though they were identical in layout—railroad flats—they were dissimilar in everything else. For one thing, my grandparents paid eighteen dollars a month rent; we paid twenty-two. For another, their apartment was warmer in winter than ours. Both were heated by coal stoves; my grandparents had a short, fat, pot-bellied one in which they burned wood which my grandfather hacked into suitable lengths each morning from the crates he'd picked up on the streets the day before; ours was bigger, more streamlined, and used real coal, purchased in burlap bags and kept in its original containers in the hall between the two apartments. Stray more than a couple of feet away from the red-hot Martana stove, and frostbite attacked the extremities; the Tarantola stove seemed to suffuse warmth the length and breadth of all four rooms. Every October, my mother had to curtain off the "front room" on our side of the hall with a thick yellow bedspread. As I held the kitchen chair on which she strained her thin body upward to hang the spread, she always recalled the days in Newark.

"Foot Number Thirteen sentenced us the day before we moved, Tommy. Do you remember him?"

I knew that Foot Number Thirteen was my mother's nickname for a myopic, ungainly boy named Salvatore Terminus who'd lived downstairs from us and whose father had changed the family name from Termino to "make it sound more American." At the age of ten, Salvatore already had such large feet that he wore size thirteen shoes. Who could forget him? I remembered his little brother Mikie, too, because I'd sometimes played with him in the yard, under my mother's watchful eye. In New York she did not allow me to play out of doors. I was taken for walks to the Five and Ten, and on summer days that weren't too hot I could play on the fire escape.

"The day before we returned to New York, Foot Number Thirteen asked me why we were leaving," my mother would go on. "I told him, 'Eh, Salvatore, this wood house, it's too cold.' 'Mrs. Martana,' he said, 'it's cold everyplace.' He sentenced us."

My grandmother, though steeped in the Sicilian beliefs in witchcraft, omens, and curses, had a less occult explanation for the temperature difference between our two apartments. "The steam heat from the big building next door helps warm our rooms. You have nothing but empty space on your side, so the wind blows through your walls."

It was true that, on our side, Denerstein's Iron Works occupied a building of only a single story, but this did not explain why our apartment should be stifling in summer, while my grandparents' was swept by cooling breezes. Under these conditions, it was natural that our family spent most of its waking hours across the hall, in "the other house."

It was sparsely furnished. That was another difference. We had regular furniture on our side: Grand Rapids bedroom, living room, and kitchen suites. The other house had more trunks in it than anything else, as though the tenants were on the verge of a long trip. Indeed, long before I was born, the Tarantolas had crossed and recrossed the Atlantic eight times in ten years, before my grandfather decided that the Statue of Liberty was to be trusted. My grandmother was convinced that Carnival Face's indecision had doomed them to a life of failure in the new world. She felt that had they come here and stayed put, the way any decent immigrant should, their fortune would have been made and they would long since have moved to the suburban splendor of Canarsie. She further observed that her conquest of America had not been helped by my grandfather's retirement from the Department of Sanitation at the age of fifty.

Four kinds of scarred linoleum distinguished the rooms of the other house. In the bright front room it was the color of overripe bananas. The room contained four heavy wood kitchen chairs, two against each of the side walls, a ramshackle bureau between the two uncurtained windows, and two trunks. In the large bedroom, the linoleum was the color of the East River. In the room were a metal double bed, a creaking wooden closet, and a trunk. In the smaller adjacent bedroom, where the linoleum lightened to the color of laundry bluing, were a cot, a chair, a trunk, and two windows. One was just a large squarish hole, opening onto the large bedroom. The other had frosted-glass panes, the top one permanently lowered, and commanded an impressive view of the huge kitchen. The kitchen was the center of activity for both houses. In addition to the gigantic table, it was furnished with chairs, a primitive gas range, an icebox, a sink, the stove, and a squat tub standing on gracefully curved legs in which clothes and, less frequently, people, were washed. When not in use, the tub was covered by a heavy metal slab, painted white, on which rested a breadbox and kitchen utensils. The linoleum in the kitchen was too threadbare to yield any hint of its original color.

Next to the sink was the small door to the *beckowzu*, a Sicilianization of "backhouse." Behind it was just enough space for a toilet bowl and a thin person. Since none of us was fat, we managed to maintain our regularity modestly. But my grandmother often wondered aloud about what happened in the first floor apartment of The Elephant.

To the left of the toilet was the front door. On it were four kinds of locks. Three times during the years we lived across the hall, thieves tried to rob the other house. Twice they were routed by the locks, and abandoned their burglar tools. The third thief had apparently been routed by my grandfather. But eventually, the other house was violated and despoiled. By then, both my grandparents were dead, the Martanas were long gone from Top Floor Left, and Filippo was rusticating on Staten Island after having sold the building to a Puerto Rican. The other house was steam-heated and furnished in relative elegance. Aunt Pina lived there alone. When she returned from work one day, her two portable radios, record player, and stack of records were missing. She moved out soon after.

The apartments in Filippo's building had both front and back doors. The "back door" to the other house led into its front room. In contrast to the kitchen door, it didn't have a single lock, but it would have taken a wrecker's ball to open. Layers of paint and years of disuse had it stuck shut, and except for a crack of space at the top and a protrusion halfway down which had been a doorknob, it fused imperceptibly into the wall.

There was one more door in the apartment—between the two bedrooms. This one was closed only when one of the family, usually Aunt Pina, felt the need of a full-scale bath in the kitchen tub. On these occasions, my grandfather sat stiffly among us in the front room, into which he otherwise seldom ventured, looking sadly dispossessed. For it was he who, night and most of the day, occupied the cot in the small bedroom adjoining the kitchen. The big bed was for my grandmother and Pina.

What most upset my father about living in the building were the meager facilities for pursuing the personal hygiene to which he'd become accustomed. He hated having to bathe in the kitchen. And the *beckowzu* on our side of the hall, otherwise identical to the one in the other house, was made even less inviting by a ledge along the right wall on which even a person as short as my father could crack his head in a distracted moment. Though it probably would have been a simple matter to remove the ledge, no one ever did.

The bathroom we had left behind in Newark seemed, by contrast, a place of pagan splendor. There had been a bathtub, a sink, a toilet, a large medicine cabinet, and a window. The floor was of small gray hexagonal tiles. On some mornings, according to my mother, the bathroom was too cold for me to enter, but most of the time, I could watch my father shave in there. From a bottle he kept in the cabinet, he always poured himself a shot of scotch before brushing lather on to his face. He sipped throughout his shave and as a special conspiratorial treat, I was allowed the last few drops. I enjoyed the taste of Palmolive with which the glass was by then flavored. After my drink I was occasionally allowed to remain in the bathroom while he bathed. My mother never liked it.

"Did he give you whiskey to drink?" she used to ask. "He's teaching you to be a drunkard like himself. Did he let you see him naked, too?"

Eventually, I became less enthusiastic about being in the bathroom with him, and by the time we moved to New York, the thought of being in any room with him made me nervous. When, shortly after the move, he decided to come home from his waiter's job in Newark only on his day off, my mother and I both felt a lot better. He'd arrive Sunday at about midnight, and immediately turn on the radio in our kitchen very loud, as though to chide us for not waiting up for him. I don't know whether my mother ever fell asleep before his arrival, but Vinnie and I always lay awake in the bed we shared, waiting for his

blast of sound. Monday afternoons after school, I stayed
out of his sight as much as I could. Monday nights we
always had the company of uncles Nick and Charlie and
their families to occupy his attention. And Tuesday mornings, my mother had already taken me to school before he
got up to go back to Newark.

It was a grand occasion whenever one or more of the
trunks in the other house were opened. I revelled in the
musty smell, watching my mother and grandmother taking
out yellowed linens, silken embroideries, and wrinkled,
noisy paper bags filled with rusted kitchen utensils, and
listening to them talk as they searched for whatever
blanket or pillowcase they were after.

One Tuesday evening, after they'd finished work on the
coats from *Li Roggispiti*, they went into the front room
to open a trunk.

"I don't think we put the album in there," my mother
said, as my grandmother lifted the lid. "I'm sure it's across
the hall, but when he asked me for it this morning, he
already had raised his shoulder halfway to the ceiling."

My father's left shoulder was slightly lower than the
right, an occupational defect of waiters. When he was
angry, he seldom raised his voice, but he raised his right
shoulder still higher.

"When he raises that shoulder," my mother went on,
"who can see straight any more? The devil is about and
clouds the eyes. Why he wants those pictures anyway, I
don't know. A lot he cares for his sons. If he cared for them,
he'd be home to see them in person and not have to look

31

at their pictures. And who knows what harlot's eyes will feast upon them as well."

My grandmother looked up from the trunk. "Have you found his handkerchiefs smeared with *lippisticchiu* again?"

"No, they're just filled with his snot now. He undoubtedly has warned his whores to wash their mouths before they come to see him. And hurrah for Novarka, New Jossi! First we had to drag him there, and now we can't get him away."

I had never heard the full story. "Why did we move to Newark in the first place?" I asked.

"Because your father lost four thousand dollars in six months with his coffeepot," my mother said contemptuously. "He had to open that coffeepot. He wouldn't rest until he had 'put our money in circulation.' He said that in America 'Money should work, not stuff a mattress.' It was Nino Orlando, Missing Note, who gave him such excommunicated ideas."

"Nino Orlando got what he deserved," my grandmother reflected. "*God does not sleep forever.*"

"Nino Orlando was not punished until his wife died of the humiliation of his desertion and their children were scattered to the four winds," my mother answered.

"The ancients said, *The bad year may be late in coming, but it always comes.* Apropos of Missing Note, observe one of his works." So saying, my grandmother pulled a large paper-wrapped parcel from the trunk and dropped it heavily to the floor. "The meat grinder I bought from him when he had *that* store. It is large enough to have kept the Papal Guard in sausage every Friday until the world conflagration. But I bought it for the sake of his poor wife and because he was a *paisano*. So they could have enough money to grind some sausage of their own."

"Did he have that store in between the grocery and the music shop?" my mother asked hesitantly.

"What are you thinking of? You're thinking of the religious articles store. He had already turned Protestant when he opened the butcher supply store, Satan incarnate that he was."

It sounded as though again I wasn't to hear the full story. "So Missing Note is responsible for our moving to Newark?" I interjected.

"Missing Note," my grandmother said, "ha-ha, even the little one knows his true name. Do you know, my *Gaetanneddu*, how he came to be called that?"

I did, but I also knew that wouldn't stop my grandmother. Once more she went through the tale of how the Orlandos and the Martanas and Tarantolas had exchanged frequent visits in the days before I'd been born; of how one of Nino's favorite means of entertaining guests had been to sit at his player piano and pretend that it was not mechanically operated but produced its melodies through the agency of his deft, gleamingly beringed fingers; and of how later he would play operatic records on his Victrola while he sang along, boasting that he was "but one note short" of being another Caruso.

Then she added the inevitable coda of how for years after he left home no one knew what had become of Nino Orlando until the day when she saw him near the *Roggispiti* store, emerging from under the hood of a sidewalk camera. He had just snapped a picture of a Negro boy on a pony. "To what depths did Missing Note fall," she concluded. "He was reduced to photographing Africans on horseback."

I tried again. "Did Missing Note ever visit us in Newark?" I asked.

"He did, the first years, when you were still too young to remember," my mother replied. "After all, you were still a baby in my arms when we moved there. You were not yet born the day your uncle Charlie came to the park where I was with your grandmother. Ah, my darling son, if your father had been a real man he would never have allowed Missing Note to talk him into that coffeepot. But he could not rest with that four thousand dollars. First he was going to open this store, then that. He put fifty dollars down on one and lost the deposit. I didn't care about the fifty dollars. But he finally had to do it. 'Now you're in business,' Nino Orlando told him. Business! Soon he had only fifteen hundred dollars of the four thousand left. I never wanted to put that money in the bank, Tommy. People watch you. They came to the house, a man and a woman. And your uncle Charlie came to call me in the park. 'Santina,' he said, 'there are two people who say they want to talk to Mario.' I felt you tighten inside me."

I didn't understand what she meant by that last remark, but I was glad she'd gotten back to the story.

"When I got home I recognized them for the devils they were. 'We want to speak to Mario Martana,' the woman said. She was a painted whore who smoked cocaine cigarettes. 'Mario Martana is my husband,' I told her. 'What do you want of him?' 'Dear lady,' the man said, 'we understand your spouse owns a small restaurant in an excellent location. We want to buy it. We wish to speak to him. Can you tell us where he is?' He had a mustache, like Satan. Who could prevail against such evil? I told him your father was in his accursed coffeepot and gave them the address. Then the cocaine smoking woman looked at my stomach and asked if they could take me for a ride in their car with them to see your father. I told them I was not one to ride in automobiles. 'Very well, *signora*,' she said. That was the last I ever saw of them, and I did not see your father for three days. After you were born, I discovered the milk had congealed in my right breast. I could offer you my left breast only."

Was there a Sicilian proverb concerning the plight of a baby thus nourished? But I did not interrupt.

"After three days there was a phone call in the meat market downstairs. The butcher came to call me and said it was your father. When I picked up that damned instrument, your father told me he wasn't coming home. There would be no point to it, he said. He had no money left. They had given him cocaine cigarettes to smoke and barrels of liquor to drink and they asked him to take the fifteen hundred dollars out of the bank and give it to them. *They* were going to buy the coffeepot and he had to give *them* the money. That's how smart your father has been all his life. The next morning he gave them the money and they told him to meet them at a hotel where they could complete their transaction. He went there, but they never appeared. He waited for two days and then he called me. I told him to come home.

"It would have been better if he had not. I used to find him drunk on the floor every night when I came home from the park with your grandmother. Then your godfather said there was an empty apartment in the building where he lived in Newark. He said your father must leave New York immediately, if he wasn't to leave it in a coffin."

"Here it is," my grandmother interrupted. "I told you so." She had emptied one trunk and had opened another, where the family album was lying right on top. "I remembered that as soon as you came back you put this here."

"So we will let him pick the pictures he wants. Next week he can pick them out and take them back to his precious Newark. I doubt that he pisses in the sink over there."

"What?" my grandmother shouted, slamming down the trunk lid.

"I found him pissing in the sink today, when I returned from leaving Tommy at school."

"What? What did you do?"

"I did nothing. I said nothing. He said nothing either, until he was opening the door to leave. He told me he couldn't go into the *beckowzu* without slamming his head. So now my sink has become a pisspot."

"It's a good thing you drain the pasta in *my* sink," my grandmother observed.

"Foot Number Thirteen cursed me," my mother said in reply.

36

THE TESTS

I was a "delicate child," underweight, underheight, and overwrought. My eyes were myopic, my teeth full of holes. I suffered from frequent headaches, toothaches, earaches, stomach-aches, heart palpitations, colds, dizzy spells, and nosebleeds. My mother applied compresses to my head, salted water to my teeth, and kisses to my face. For my stomach-aches, she had me drink hot water flavored with bay leaves. To stop my nosebleeds, she placed crossed knives on my bare knees. To open my nasal passages, she had me inhale hot olive oil. To strengthen my vision, she prayed to St. Lucy. To alleviate all my other infirmities, she sprinkled me from a jar that at one time had held olives but now contained Holy Water, personally gathered by me on our annual pilgrimage to a place called The Lourdes of the Bronx. She walked me to school every morning, called for me at noon, took me back after lunch, and called for me again at three o'clock.

The school, P.S. 85, was located at the corner of First Avenue and 117th Street, in a building much older than the one which housed the Fourteenth Avenue School in

37

Newark. "But it is much closer," my mother said. "I have only Second Avenue to cross." She crossed it eight times a day, and negotiated a total of twenty-four flights of stairs. When my grandmother suggested once that I might manage to cross Second Avenue by myself, my mother grew so angry that the subject was never again mentioned.

P.S. 85 was different from the Fourteenth Avenue School in other ways. In the first place, instead of incorporating eight grades, in my mother's words, "it only arrived at the sixth." Secondly, it was not co-educational. "Better that way," my mother said. "Boys in one school, girls in another. Both will learn more." And, thirdly, it was served by a visiting physician.

In my first week there, our 3B teacher, Mrs. Bender, announced that it was time for our physical examination by Dr. Baumgart to whose office we were to proceed in "size place." (In Newark, whenever we'd lined up for anything, it had been alphabetically.)

So, escorted by Mrs. Bender, and clutching my "health card," I led my first line, proceeding gingerly to Dr. Baumgart's "office," a gloomy basement room, decorated with lockers along three of its walls.

"All right, son, let's have your card and open your mouth," Dr. Baumgart said when I approached. He had gray, closely cropped hair, a droopy mustache, bags under his eyes, and a tongue depressor in his hand.

"My God," he exclaimed, "open wider." He shook his head and clucked. "Where do you come from, er, Martana?"

I told him I was from Newark, New Jersey.

"Didn't they ever examine your teeth there?"

"Sometimes."

"Sometimes? Sometimes. Sometime before you're twenty-one, your last tooth will have dropped out of your mouth. Already your new adult teeth are full of caries. And your remaining milk teeth are just disgusting."

He gave my tongue a disgusted jab with his depressor and told me he was writing a note to my parents and making a notation on my record. "I want to see you again in two weeks," he continued. "If I don't find evidence in your mouth that you've started a course of treatment, I'm not going to permit you to continue in school. Now step over to the eye chart and read the last line."

Reading the last line had been easy in Newark: I'd simply repeated the responses of sharp-eyed Carmela Malerba. But here I had to admit to Dr. Baumgart that I couldn't see the last line. He asked me to read the smallest line I could see.

"I can't see any of the lines," I confessed. "Just the top letter. It's a capital E."

"Well, where are your glasses, Martino? Don't tell me you don't have glasses."

I told him.

"I suppose they sometimes examined your eyes in Newark, too," he shouted. The kids in line behind me began snickering while Dr. Baumgart added a postscript to his note and another notation to my record. "Same thing goes," he said. "If you don't come back here with glasses in two weeks, no school for you. Look, if your parents can't afford to take you to your own dentist or oculist, they can take you to a clinic. Understand? It's free. God, I don't know which is worse, your eyes or your spaghetti-and-olive-oil teeth. Now take off your shirt."

Since my mother did not trust a belt to do the whole job of keeping me decent, taking off my shirt meant unbuttoning it from my knickers. I started to do this, to the uncontrolled hilarity of my classmates. Dr. Baumgart shouted at them to be quiet. Almost gently, he said to leave my shirt on and pointed to a bench on which he said I should sit. "I'm going to examine the rest of the class first," he said. "You need a little special attention."

I sat for a long time beside Mrs. Bender, watching the shoes of my classmates file past me. "Now, you get those things attended to, Thomas," my teacher advised. "You heard what Dr. Baumgart said. When you get through here, see that he gives you a corridor pass and hurry back to class."

A few minutes after she and the rest of the class had left, Dr. Baumgart beckoned me.

"Okay, what's-your-name, take off your shirt. Unbutton your underwear, too."

He put his stethoscope to my chest and asked me to breathe deeply.

"Deeper. Again. Again. Deeper. Again. Breathe deeply, don't be afraid. Hold it."

He looked concerned, and asked me to breathe deeply some more. I breathed so deeply so rapidly that I began to choke.

"You have a murmur," Dr. Baumgart said. "What we call functional, probably."

So I was destined to die of a heart attack, even before my teeth fell out and I went blind.

"Don't worry about it. Put your shirt back on and get to your class. Take the note home and don't forget what I said. In two weeks you'll be wearing glasses and have started dental treatment, or out you go. And when you come back, I may decide to refer you to a clinic for an electrocardiogram just to make sure the murmur's functional. We'll see. We'll talk about it."

He wrote out my pass and I headed back to class, walking upstairs as slowly as possible so as not to put undue strain on my failing heart.

"We've been holding up the audiometer test until you got back, Thomas," Mrs. Bender informed me the instant I walked diffidently into the room. She handed me a printed form and a pair of earphones and told me to take my seat. With the eyes of all 3B upon me, I did so, suddenly doubting that I'd succeeded in rebuttoning all my buttons correctly. While Mrs. Bender explained how we were to affix our earphones, I slipped my right hand inside my shirt, to monitor my sick, erratic heartbeats.

A few seconds after my earphones were in place, I heard a reedy male voice whisper: "Please write the numbers you hear in the first column on the left-hand side of your paper. Three-seven, Four-swish. Hiss-two, Shss-brssh." The voice grew softer and less intelligible and finally inaudible. There was a long static-punctuated wait, before an even reedier and less distinct female voice commanded: "Now write the numbers you hear in the first column on the right-hand side of your paper. Nyun-fouh, Shix-wish, Misth-tish." Her

41

voice died out more quickly than the man's. I had to guess at most of the numbers. Now I was sure that, along with all my other infirmities, I was deaf, too.

On completion of this last ordeal, Mrs. Bender announced that, a sound body having been assured, we would be tested soon for something she called our I.Q. It was nearly noon now, she said, too late to do any work, so we were free to talk quietly among ourselves till the bell rang. Normal work, she said, would resume in the afternoon. I felt certain that, for me, normal work would never resume.

I was surprisingly self-controlled on my way home, as I told my mother all that had happened, but once there, I started to cry.

"You won't go back this afternoon," my mother consoled. "You will rest at home."

I was calm until after dinner, when I began crying again. "They have to put drops in my eyes," I whined. "Some kids say you can't see for a week afterwards."

"Don't worry," my mother reassured. "You're not going to *l'occhialista* with The Standard Bearer; you're going with me. No one will put poisons into your eyes. And don't worry about the dentist. I'll take you to Dr. Connovi on Saturday. I used to go to his mother-in-law when I had to have teeth pulled. She never let me feel any pain, *la dottoressa Filomena*. Ask your grandmother."

"Enchanted hands," my grandmother agreed.

My mother nodded. "When she got too old, she recommended that we go to Dr. Connovi. He'd just married her daughter then. This was about two years before you were born."

"Two years?" My grandmother shook her head. "What are you saying, Santina? Your son was born in April of nineteen thirty-two." She lowered her voice and explained, "Carnival Face returned to Camporeale for the fourth time in September of nineteen twenty-eight, the day after I had the last two teeth at the back of the right side of my mouth pulled. I remember I was still bleeding the next day, and I waved to him with a bloody handkerchief. Would that it had been *his* blood, from a hemorrhage. But it was Dr. Connovi who pulled my teeth. In September of nineteen twenty-eight. September sixteenth. Carnival Face sailed on the seventeenth. *Seventeen means misfortune,* the ancients said. They were right. His ship did not sink, to my misfortune. Listen to him snore in there now on that cot, the pasta not yet cold in his stomach."

"But," I sobbed, "I also have heart trouble."

"Don't worry," my mother soothed. "We'll pray to the Lord and to His Blessed Mother. *The good have to suffer, but they will prevail. All evil does not come to harm.*"

She dried my tears and hugged me to her. My grandmother busied herself with her homework, and my brother, who had heard everything in silence, went across the hall to play the radio. I rested in my mother's arms, listening to her heartbeats, which seemed nearly as rapid as mine. Finally she nudged me gently and said firmly, "The best thing to do is to get started. Let us go get you some glasses. There's a place on Third Avenue that's open at night. Nothing bad is going to happen."

When we entered Golden's Optometrists-Opticians, she

greeted Mr. Golden with the note from Dr. Baumgart and the stern injunction, "No droppisi."

"No drops, no drops. Joosta glasses. S'okay, mama, no worry," Mr. Golden assured us, in burlesque Italian accent.

I had my glasses within a week. In fact, we picked them up on Saturday morning, on our way to the dentist's. They made all straight edges look round. I stepped off rounded curbs, trudged by rounded store fronts, and looked up at rounded fire escapes as we headed for 106th Street. I told my mother that the glasses were very strong and were making me dizzy. She assured me I'd get used to them. "Now we'll get this other thing over with, and then there will be nothing to worry about."

Except for my heart, I thought, putting my right hand on my chest for possibly the five-hundredth time since my examination by Dr. Baumgart.

Dr. Connovi's office was one flight up in a grimy corner building. My mother opened the door, causing a bell to chime, and preceded me down a narrow, linoleum-covered corridor, at the end of which was an empty waiting room. A pleasant, young-looking woman wearing a spotless white uniform pulled open a pair of French doors and limped to greet us. On her shriveled right leg, she wore a high black shoe on a platform. Through the open doors behind her I could see two dentist's chairs and terrifying appliances.

"Ah, *signora* Martana," the woman said in Neapolitan-accented Italian, "so many years I have not seen you."

"*Buon giorno*," my mother answered. "I have come on account of my son. They have given him warnings in school."

44

"Oh, we'll take care of that," the woman said to me in English. "What happened, they gave you a note?"

I nodded and she smiled. "Don't be afraid," she said, "nobody's going to hurt you. Doctor should be here soon. Let me see what they wrote."

I translated her request for my mother, who handed her the by-now slightly tattered note. She looked at it for a second, before asking me to follow her beyond the French doors. "Do you want your mother with you, Thomas? *Signora*, you can come inside if you want to."

She looked into my mouth without betraying the slightest disgust. She touched some teeth lightly with a thin, straight instrument which my new glasses rounded out every time it approached me.

"You have bad teeth," she said. "I'll bet you get lots of toothaches." Her cool, dry hand touched my cheek lightly.

I smiled shyly. "Sometimes."

"You don't have a toothache now, do you?"

I shook my head. No, I didn't have a toothache. I was dizzy, but it didn't matter because the way my heart was beating, it wouldn't hold out much longer.

The dentist made a noisy, cursing entrance, apparently dropping something in the corridor. While he greeted my mother with ostentatious enthusiasm, I noticed that his glasses were much more impressive than mine. They were closed at the sides, like goggles. He was bald, nervous, and drooled slightly from the corners of his mouth.

"Here, Jerko," he said, handing his assistant a bulky brown bag, "put this away. The Queen of Sheba can't do

45

her own shopping. I think I busted her balls, I mean I think I busted her eggs." He laughed vociferously, quieted immediately, and asked, "Who else is coming today, Jerko?" as his assistant was still limping around trying to find a place to put the bag.

"Uh, the Scalisi woman," she said, flustered.

"The one on home relief with fourteen children and three teeth? What the hell am I doing for her?"

"Final impressions for her plates."

"That's what she thinks. Stall her. I'm getting out of here as soon as I finish this. These people are lucky they caught me. Why the hell don't you put the bag down, Jerko?"

He grabbed it from her and propped it up in the empty dentist's chair to my right.

"Aha," he said, turning his attention toward me. "How do you do, young man. Anybody named Martana or Tarantola or Martanola or Tarantana is a friend of mine." He shook my hand and confronted his assistant again. "What have you done for him?"

"I examined his mouth. He has a note from school."

"You examined his mouth?" Dr. Connovi said with mock awe. "Are you a dentist, miss? Did you graduate from N. Y. Jew?" Then, in a confidential tone, he told me, "I taught Miss Jerko everything she knows. Now she thinks she's a dentist." Next, he whirled on my mother, who was hovering behind me. "Outside, *signora*, please."

"He's a little nervous," my mother said in her best Italian. "It would make him feel better if I stayed with him, Doctor."

46

"You want to stay, stay. You sure nobody else is coming, Jerko?"

"Just the Scalisi woman."

"What about what's-his-name? What about Mikey Fat?"

"I don't know who you're talking about," Miss Jerko answered.

"Isn't he your boy friend? Excuse me, I thought he was coming. Doesn't he always come when he sees you? Jerko, you've been examining his mouth, where's his chart?"

Her face aflame, she handed him the card on which she'd been making marks between probes into my mouth. "I was almost finished when you came in," she said.

"He's been here two hours, then. Open your mouth, mister. Open, open, open, what the hell are you afraid of? Holy Christ! Your mouth looks like a Sicilian shithouse! *Signora*, do you know what your son's mouth is like? Step over here and take a look."

My mother took a peek and nodded gingerly.

"*Bello, quant'e bello*," Dr. Connovi said. "*Signora*, do you want me to look at yours, too?"

My mother lied that it would not be necessary because her teeth were all right.

"I'm not talking about your teeth," Dr. Connovi said, and laughed uproariously. Now my mother's face was as red as Miss Jerko's.

"Take off your glasses, son," Dr. Connovi said, quieting down. "I'll give you an injection and we'll pull the first, maybe two."

Everything was straight and fuzzy again as I waited for the needle.

"*Sicilia bella, bella Sicilia,*" Dr. Connovi sang loudly as my mother placed her hand on my brow and Miss Jerko held onto my left hand. "My wife's Sicilian, God bless her. The Queen of Sheba." He grimaced and grunted. I twitched and whimpered as the pain of the needle reverberated in my heart.

"Okay, Jerko, let go of him and get my coffee. *Signora, una tazza di caffe?* We have a few minutes before the injection takes effect." Never moving her hand from my damp forehead, my mother declined with thanks.

Dr. Connovi pulled not one, not two, but three teeth, sweating and drooling with the effort. On our way home, my mouth was still stuffed with cotton to absorb the blood.

"He's a good dentist, even though he likes to jest," my mother said. "Did it hurt?"

I shook my head No.

A month later, I'd gotten used to my glasses. Dr. Connovi, whom my mother took me to visit weekly, had stopped pulling for a while and had started filling. But I was still waiting for my heart attack. Dr. Baumgart, pleased with the glasses and with the wounds in my mouth, had assured me that my audiometer test results showed I had normal hearing. But he'd forgotten to say anything about my heart or about sending me for an electrocardiogram. I hadn't reminded him.

I waited for my attack mainly at night, in bed, after Vinnie had begun snoring. An anxious smoldering would start at the base of my spine and work its way inexorably up and around to set my chest on fire. With my hand, I'd feel my heart thumping, then I'd turn over on my left side to hear it on my pillow. I'd pray to Jesus, to Mary, to all the saints I knew. Eventually I'd feel a flutter, and I'd know the end was at hand. I'd fall asleep not expecting to awaken. I suffered in silence, saying nothing to my mother about it, letting her believe I'd been cured by the Lourdes of the Bronx Holy Water. Not until the start of my second semester in P.S. 85, in January of 1941, did I have to tell her the matter was still in doubt. Dr. Baumgart had examined us again and asked me how my heart was. I told him it was okay. He looked at my record and said he'd never gotten the results of my cardiogram. I told him I'd never had one, because he hadn't sent me.

And so, a few days later, once more clutching a note, my mother escorted me to a clinic downtown. I'd been excused from school for the morning. All I remember of the electrocardiogram procedure is that the cream which was applied to my ankles and wrists produced almost the same kind of burning sensation that started in my back every night.

I'd become something of a class curiosity by the next week, when Dr. Baumgart informed me, offhandedly, that the results of the electrocardiogram showed nothing wrong with my heart. My celebrity had been caused by Miss Fleischman, my 4A teacher, who, the morning of my trip to the clinic, had told my classmates how unusual it was to have someone like Thomas Martana in their class. Someone with an I.Q. of one hundred sixty-five.

THE GAMES

Despite my precariously balanced health and high I.Q., I was, along with my brother, athletically minded.

Every Friday night during the fall, Vinnie would print a list of all the big college football games on a sheet of the "drawing paper" I liked so much—Herald Square Typewriter Paper, bought for me regularly by my mother at the Five and Ten. The following morning, we "picked the winners" my brother indicating his choices with asterisks, and I with circles. That night, we'd get most of the results from Stan Lomax on Radio Station WOR. Those scores that hadn't arrived in time for the program, we'd check the next day in the *Sunday News*. When all the results were listed, Vinnie added up our respective wins and losses and figured our percentages for the week. He also kept running season totals. He prided himself on his winning percentage, higher than those of some "experts" in the *News*, higher even than Stan Lomax's. Mine was much lower, most of my picks being based on emotion. I hated the University of Southern California, for example, for reasons I can't remember, and always picked them to lose. On the other hand, I loved and always picked as winners the Duke "Blue Devils," the Michigan "Wolverines," and the Fordham "Rams." This method of selection, although disastrous over a season, sometimes enabled me to beat out my brother on a given week. On those occasions, my joy was unconfined.

But this kind of excitement lasted only from Friday night until Sunday morning, and for just a couple of months. We were interested in professional football hardly at all, although we did listen to the Giant games. Similarly, our interest in hockey was limited to radio listening and to batting around a button we made believe was a puck with two of my toy soldiers as the hockey players.

Baseball was different. It kept all the men of the Martanas and Tarantolas keyed up from April until early October. Vinnie and I were Yankee fans, my father was a Yankee and Dodger fan, my uncles Nick and Charlie were primarily Giant fans. Even my grandfather took an interest in Joe DiMaggio and Frank Crosetti.

For me, the baseball season meant, among other things, that there was *The Daily Bugle* to get out Monday through Friday. *The Daily Bugle* was a newspaper I wrote, edited, and printed in pencil on half a sheet of my typewriter paper. It had a circulation of one: my brother. He read it immediately upon his return from work in a factory where he packed tomatoes. This job had confirmed my grandparents in their low opinion of American education. My grandmother insisted that alumnae of Camporeale's third grade were better educated than American high school graduates, and my grandfather, who'd never gone to school at all, said, "In Sicily, one is already a notary public before he graduates from the low school. What kind of work for a scholar and graduate of the high school is arranging four tomatoes into a cardboard box?"

It was the kind of work that paid Vinnie ten dollars a week and sent him home every night with his scholarly hands sore and full of little cuts. Into those hands, I thrust *The Daily Bugle*. I'd gotten the idea for it when, the first night he came home from work, he asked me if I knew what the Yankees had done that afternoon. The following night, I not only had the Yankee score for him, on paper, but the scores of all the other ball games in both leagues, as well as home runs, pitching performances, and highlights of play—the result of an afternoon's intensive radio listening. Vinnie was pleased and told me I was a regular Grantland Rice. I kept the paper going even during the part of the season I had to go to school. I had fewer facts about the early innings of games in those issues and more highflown prose.

The season also meant that Sundays, in late morning and early afternoon, I could look out of one of the front windows of the other house and watch the stickball games. If the weather was too hot, I couldn't watch uninterruptedly because, even though my head was protected by an imitation Yankee hat my mother had bought for me at the Five and Ten, she was afraid too much sun would incapacitate me. But the shouts of the players would always draw me back to the window to see the conclusion of any exciting plays occurring during my absences so that, all in all, I didn't miss much.

The Games

The games pitted the young men from our block, 117th Street between Second and Third avenues, against those from other blocks in the neighborhood. They were played for money, which changed hands immediately after the last man was out. They were usually watched by a couple of dozen people arrayed along the sidewalk, but they and all the players and their broom-handle bats disappeared within seconds whenever the catcher gave the alarm that a police car was approaching.

Occasionally, my pretty aunt Pina squeezed in beside me at the window to watch part of a game. If one of the players saw her, most of the others would soon start looking up too, winking and smiling. Pina would make a remark about how they were all a bunch of jerks and go back inside. Along about the fifth or sixth inning of most games, I'd see my grandmother returning from Mass, walking warily, close to the buildings.

"They are ravening like mad dogs," she'd puff when she got upstairs. "It isn't safe on the streets with them. *Bessibolla*, the devil's pastime."

For my father and brother, the season of the devil's pastime also meant an occasional trip to Yankee Stadium. My father did not go as often as my brother, since his day off, Monday, was frequently a day off for baseball teams as well, while there were always games on weekends for my brother to attend. Sometimes Pina went with him and they'd sit in the right-field bleachers, where she could blow kisses at the pitchers in the Yankee bullpen. It was after one such outing that Vinnie returned home with a gift for me: a miniature baseball bat, about fifteen inches long, with Joe DiMaggio's signature reproduced on it. It was a lovely thing, a perfect scale model, stained dark brown.

"Let's play baseball," I said impulsively.

"Okay," Vinnie answered, "where's the dice?"

He was referring to one of the other things the season meant for me: the nightly baseball game of Vinnie's invention which required no physical exertion beyond that needed to roll a pair of dice. Each number represented a different baseball play. Snake eyes was a home run, three a triple, four a double, five a strike-out, six a fly-out, seven a single, eight a ground-out, nine a foul-out, ten a double play (or ground-out if nobody was on base), eleven a walk, and twelve an error. Vinnie would write the line-up of the Yankees on one side of a sheet of the typewriter paper, and the line-up of the opposition, which I was free to choose, on the other. He invariably made one change in the Yankee line-up—he benched DiMaggio and inserted himself as clean-up hitter. I liked to be lead-off man for my team. Across the top of the sheet we kept score. Once a week we calculated won-and-lost standings, batting averages, earned-run averages, and strike-out records.

"No, I mean with the bat," I said. "For real."

"What do you mean for real? You can't go downstairs. Besides, it's not a real bat. It's way too small."

"It's just my size," I said, "and we can play in the other house."

"Inside?"

"Sure, inside. They don't have any furniture we have to worry about breaking, do they?"

I could see the idea appealed to him.

54

"We could make a ball out of paper and tie it up with string. A real ball would bounce too much," he said.

"Yeah, I'll get some newspaper."

"Nah. Your typewriter paper's better. It'll make a stronger ball."

Vinnie crumpled a sheet of it tightly, then wrapped another sheet around it. The typewriter paper made an exciting crackling sound in his big hands. It took four sheets to achieve the desired circumference. By that time we were in the other house, and I was asking in Sicilian, "Ma, have you got any string?"

"In the breadbox," she said. "What are you going to do?"

"We're going to play *bessi-bolla.*"

"*Bessi-bolla,*" my grandmother said. "Inside?"

"Yes."

"Why don't you play in your house?"

"There's more room here," said Vinnie, tying the ball together.

"Be careful. Don't get tired. Don't sweat," my mother said to me.

"I'll be the Yankees," Vinnie said. "You?"

"The Dodgers."

"Okay, we're playing in New York so I'm the home team. You're up first."

Vinnie stood by the foot of the bed in the large bedroom, ready to release the first pitch, as I took my batting stance between the two front-room windows with the bureau serving as backstop.

"Wait a minute," Vinnie said. He cupped his hands over his mouth and in a theatrical voice announced: "Attention please, ladies and gentlemen. The batteries for today's game. For the Brooklyn Dodgers: Wyatt and Owen. For the New York Yankees: Ruffing and Dickey. Play ball!"

The first pitch was by me before I knew what had happened. I prepared myself for the next one, pumping the bat back and forth. I swung and missed before the ball reached me. The great Red Ruffing had thrown a slow ball. I swung and missed several more times before I finally connected on a fast ball. The bat sent a screaming foul tip backwards through the open right window.

"Don't look out," Vinnie warned, "it might have hit somebody on the head. Go get some more paper and string."

With a new ball in play and the windows lowered, he quickly retired the side.

Whitlow Wyatt was knocked out of the box in the first inning. Vinnie hit every pitch I threw. Line drives caromed off the bed, the trunks, the chairs, and me. They whistled through the bedroom window onto my grandfather's cot, causing the old man to snore more fitfully than usual. They sailed gracefully into the kitchen, past the ladies preparing the evening meal. Vinnie circled the bases—chair, edge of front-room linoleum, and chair—with dizzying frequency.

"What in the name of the Holy Mother of God are you doing in there?" my grandmother screamed from the kitchen. Simultaneously, we heard heavy thuds from downstairs. Filippo, who lived directly underneath the other house, was making us aware of his displeasure.

My mother appeared in the front room. She surveyed

her two perspiring sons with horror. "Stop this barbarism," she cried, "and open the windows."

"Game called on account of Mother," Vinnie whispered to me as we made our way, figuratively, to the showers.

By the next Saturday morning, my brother had devised a way to play more calmly, without running. "We'll just hit the ball," he said. "If it goes into the bedroom it'll be a single, in Grandpa's room is a double, and in the kitchen a home run."

I pointed out that he had made no provision for triples.

"On the fire escape will be a triple. Triples are harder to hit than home runs anyway."

We played while my grandfather was out for his daily walk over the Triboro Bridge, so we had one less ground rule to worry about. My grandmother, who worked at *Li Roggispiti* half a day on Saturdays, was out, too. Only my mother was around, and we assured her that our new version of baseball involved very little perspiration for us or our landlord.

Vinnie and the Yankees won the game by a lopsided score. Thereafter we played every week at the same time, just before our Saturday lunch of soup and potatoes. Although I improved to the point where I'd get a few singles a game, I was no match for Vinnie. Hope sprang eternal though, or at least sprang every Saturday morning.

"I'm gonna beat you today, you lousy Yankees." I would grit my teeth, furiously swinging the fifteen-inch bat.

"Oh, yeah?" Vinnie would smirk. "We'll mobilize you Bums."

He always did.

THE RUNAWAY

I harbored a small grudge against my aunt Pina.

The events which led up to it had started in *lu stanzinu* [the little room] in Newark. *Lu stanzinu* had served for storage of the homemade tomato sauce which my grandmother always came from New York to help bottle, and as a dumping ground for old chamberpots, worn mattresses, and Vinnie's discarded toys. Vinnie, apparently, had found another use for *lu stanzinu* as a hiding place for his small library of picture books. At least I assumed the glossy pamphlets bearing such titles as *French Femmes* and *Bare Facts* were his. My discovery of them had aroused an unusual excitement in me, as well as a strong urge to take off my clothes, like the women in the photographs. But, since a short time before, my mother had let me know that she did not approve of even partial nudity, I kept my urge, and the pictures, hidden.

My mother's warning had come on a hot day when my grandmother and Pina had been visiting. After making a tentative move at taking off my shirt, I was told that it wasn't nice to walk around that way. My aunt put up a mild argument in behalf of the body beautiful, but my mother had in addition assured her, unanswerably, that if the slightest breeze developed it would find its way to my perspiring torso, immediately incapacitating me.

Remembering Pina's intervention on that occasion, the next time she and her mother came to Newark, I was emboldened to hint at my new acquaintanceship with the bare facts. I waited until my mother and grandmother were upstairs at my godparents, the Licaris. Vinnie, Pina, and I were alone in the kitchen.

"You know," I said to my aunt, "I like to look at naked women."

She thought that was one of the funniest things she'd ever heard. "Six years old and you like to look at naked women? You're starting early. What part do you like to look at the most?"

"All the parts."

"Boy-oh-boy. It's the little quiet ones you have to watch out for. You hear this, Vinnie? You ought to take lessons from this kid."

"Shame on you, Tommy," my brother said. "You shouldn't say things like that. It's a sin."

I didn't know why he should feel that way. The picture books in *lu stanzinu* were surely his. I didn't say anything, though. It's our secret, I thought. We both like naked women.

But for me it didn't stay a secret long. When we joined our elders upstairs, Pina asked everybody, "Do you know what the little one said downstairs?" Then she told them.

There was silence, followed by general laughter. My god-father ran to quote me in his diary.

My mother said, "He's so young. What does he know about such things?"

My grandmother called me a *ricuttaru* [a ricotta dealer]. These cheese dealers were the legendary studs of Sicily.

Vinnie laughed as loudly as anyone, but I knew he was blushing nearly as much as I.

My godmother kept saying, "*Bravo, Santo Gaetano.*"

"He takes after his father," my godfather decided.

After the laughter subsided, I was told I must never again say or think such a thing.

"*Vergogna,*" said my godparents sternly. "Shame."

"How did you find out you like naked women?" my mother asked me.

I said I didn't know.

"Where have you seen them?" my grandmother demanded.

"Maybe in my dreams," I answered.

She accepted that. "*Lu diavulu vene 'nzunnu in furma di donna,*" she observed. "*The devil comes in sleep in the form of a woman.* You should wake up when you have such dreams and make the sign of the cross."

My embarrassment waned long before my resentment. In a few days I was back in *lu stanzinu* looking at naked women with my pants down; but at the time we moved back to New York I still couldn't look Pina in the eye. Fortunately, like my father, she wasn't around that much anyhow. She went out most afternoons and practically every evening, usually in answer to the summons of an automobile horn. Occasionally, I'd peek from the window at the drivers. They all looked like George Raft.

Every once in a while, I'd overhear Pina telling Vinnie about the peripheral details of her life. It was more monologue than dialogue, since Vinnie had no opinion on the relative merits of scotch versus rye or bourbon, nor could he tell a pink lady from a grasshopper. And, despite his taste in photography, he seemed equally puzzled when Pina told him of having gone to burlesque shows "with some fellows." She'd describe in detail the actions of the strippers and the jokes of the comics. Once, recalling one of the latter, she laughed herself silly at the punch line, "I put it in the queen's box." Met with my brother's silence, she asked him if he didn't know where the queen's box was. He assured her he did, but I was willing to bet he could no more pinpoint it than I could.

Pina had a girl friend named Lucille who sometimes came to the house, apparently for the purpose of helping her apply make-up. Lucille was as unattractive as Pina was beautiful. She was fat, red-haired, long of nose, and, judging from her wheezing, short of breath. My grandmother thought of her as a bad companion who was leading her daughter astray. She preached long and hard to Pina on the dangers of evil associations. Pina would respond by snapping her chewing gum and continuing to apply mascara.

My grandfather blamed his daughter's behavior on his wife. "If you were not a marked woman, she would not act as she does," he said. "One day I will let her feel the full power of my arm, as you will, my esteemed bride." Despite his threats, he not only never laid a hand on his daughter, he never even spoke angrily to her. Much as they depended on my mother, the child of their old age was the favorite of both my grandparents.

Their distress, therefore, was very great when Pina stopped coming home altogether.

For the first forty-eight hours after her disappearance, they screamed day and night. My grandfather called down imprecations not only on his wife but on us all, and my grandmother blamed everything on Lucille, in whose company Pina had last departed from the other house. "You will all land in the Bowery," my grandfather ranted. "Your sallow son Calogero, his American spouse, and their half-breed offspring; your jailbird son Nicola and that fishwife they say he will marry; your precious companion Santina, her bath-taking husband, the tomato-packing professor, the silent dwarf, and all their eyeglasses with them; and most especially you, my deformed tormentress, you will lead them all to the Bowery in procession. Blood of the potato! Blood of the Madonna! When you are in these straits I will look down from the other world and eat a chicken!"

"You will see nothing but fire and smoke when you are gone," my grandmother answered. "The hell you have made of my life will be as nothing compared to the hell awaiting you. Chicken! You will be the one roasting! You are the one who is already on the Bowery! That cot of yours is your Bowery. My daughter has vanished and you can do nothing but blaspheme. She has been spirited away by an evil woman and you do nothing but call on Satan! Forgive him, Blessed Virgin. Excommunicate him."

On the third day, my uncle Nick, through some slight acquaintanceship with one of the George Rafts who were Pina's admirers, learned Lucille's address. My grandparents and my mother immediately went to confront Lucille's father, a Neapolitan widower. As reconstructed by my mother, the confrontation was a brief one.

Demanding satisfaction, my grandparents had been answered with the story of the *cornutu* [cuckold], who, upon accusing the man he suspected of alienating his wife's affections, was told: "Your name is Minicu and my name is Minicu. You have a wife and I have a wife. You live opposite Saint Stefano's and I live opposite Saint Stefano's. You are a *cornutu* and I am a *cornutu.*"

"That's all the satisfaction they got," my mother said, rather smugly. "He told them they are both whores, one as bad as the other."

Pina and Lucille stayed away for nearly a month. It was to Lucille's father that they eventually returned.

"A childish prank," he assured my grandparents, when he escorted Pina to the other house. "And now perhaps it would be better if your daughter not see my daughter again."

"Did the assassin think *my* daughter was contaminating his whore?" my grandmother shouted later. "I should have told him just what I think of him! I should have asked him how sure he is that that Neapolitan slut *is* his daughter."

After being told she'd brought disgrace to the family, Pina was asked what she'd done, specifically. She refused to discuss it. She merely listened quietly to the fulminations of her parents and, when they were done, she issued an apparently prepared statement. The highlights of it were that she would not leave home again provided she could go out when she felt like it and with whom she felt like; that she did not feel like going out with Lucille any more because Lucille had turned out to be a drip; that if she felt like coming home after midnight, she should be allowed to do so without question and without anyone waiting up for her; and, finally, that to facilitate her comings and goings, she must receive her own key forthwith. My grandmother had one made for her the next day.

Within a couple of months of Pina's return, Lucille's place in her life was taken by a girl named Carmela Rombello. Carmela endeared herself to my grandmother the first time she visited the other house by proclaiming proudly that she was of *see-cheel-yan* parentage. Considerably better looking than Lucille, she was still not in the same league with Pina. But she seemed closer to her than Lucille had ever been. They not only went out together on Saturday nights, they came home together on Sunday mornings, always after my grandmother had already risen. They'd sleep in the big bed until the middle of the afternoon, and then they'd lie awake for at least an hour before getting up, talking in low voices about the guys they'd been out with the night before. Weekend guests were something new in our lives. The first time Carmela slept over, my mother, my grandparents, Vinnie, and I ate our Sunday noon meal of ziti and sausage in self-conscious silence out of deference to the sleeping stranger. But when it became apparent that

Carmela's visits were to be an almost weekly event, my grandmother and my mother were no longer hesitant about speaking up any time they felt like it. Carmela and Pina slept quite soundly through it all, anyhow. They slept so soundly, in fact, that after a while I conquered my reluctance to walk past their bed into the front room so I could watch the stickball games from the window. A little while after that, I even stopped averting my gaze when I passed.

There was no doubt of it. Even asleep, Pina was by far the more attractive. Carmela slept with her mouth open, usually with her right arm over her head. I found her pajama sleeve boring. Pina, on the other hand, always seemed to be smiling when she was asleep, and whenever the bed coverings were disarrayed, I could see she slept in her underwear. I found the latter so interesting that even when fall came and the stickball games stopped, I'd walk past their bed into the front room. I pretended to have important business there, but all I did was doodle on my typewriter paper while looking at the bed. So assiduous was I that it was only a question of time until I saw Pina uncovered altogether. When I did, it turned out to be more exciting even than the French femmes of *lu stanzinu*. But it was only a question of a little more time until I was caught. It was Carmela who caught me. When I saw her wake up, smile, and nudge Pina, I turned away and concentrated feverishly on my doodles. I couldn't make out what was said, but there was a lot of giggling involved.

After several minutes, my aunt called out to me, "What are you doing, Tommy?"

"Drawing," I said.

"What were you doing before?"

"I was drawing before, too." I wondered how I could possibly escape past the bed.

"You weren't looking?"

"Looking?"

"What were you looking at?"

"Nothing."

"You were looking. That's not nice, at your age. What are you drawing? Let me see what you are drawing."

I went to the bed, keeping my eyes riveted on the metal headboard.

"What's this? It's just squiggles," she said when I handed her the paper.

"I was just fooling around."

"That's what I know, you were fooling around. Stop fooling around and go inside."

She pulled the covers over herself ostentatiously. Then she turned to Carmela and told her it was the little quiet ones you had to watch out for.

THE FEASTS

Of the four holidays we observed either with pomp or solemnity, the only one we celebrated on its feast day was that of St. Lucy, on December 13. Christmas was celebrated on Christmas Eve. Easter was observed from Holy Thursday to Holy Saturday morning. And the feast of Our Lady of Mount Carmel put us into a carnival mood for a week or more, until the night before the actual holiday, July 16.

The last-named celebration centered around the Church of Our Lady of Mount Carmel on 115th Street, between First and Pleasant avenues. It was the church where my parents had been married long ago and my uncle Nick very recently; where my grandmother, mother, and I spent many winter Sunday afternoons watching others, strangers to us, get married; where my brother and I had been baptized; and where, once a year, Italians and their children were attracted from as far away as Staten Island and New Jersey. They came not only to bring candles to the church, but to eat fried foods, to ride ferris wheels and merry-go-rounds, to watch Italian radio singers perform on an outdoor stage erected on the periphery of Jefferson Park, and to follow

67

a statue of the Madonna in procession through the streets of East Harlem. The Tarantolas and Martanas came too, from 117th Street, though not all of us did all those things. Because of my mother's concern for my internal and external well-being, I was not allowed to eat at the feast, or go on the rides. Still, the time of the feast was a happy one, and I shared my elders' feelings that the day itself was anticlimactic because it signaled the end of festivity for another year.

We enjoyed the feast of Our Lady despite its having been unknown in Sicily. That it was primarily a Neapolitan devotion was explained by my grandmother as due to Mount Carmel's location just outside of Naples, somewhere near Vesuvius. The feast of St. Lucy, however, was Sicilian through and through.

It involved the severest form of penance imaginable: abstinence for an entire day from bread and pasta. To honor the holy Sicilian maiden who, it was said, had her eyes plucked out rather than submit to the carnal lusts of a heathen admirer, we ate only wheat kernels, called *cuccia*, and rice on her day. We ate the *cuccia* in milk, mixed with chocolate chips and sugar. We ate the rice with tomato sauce and cheese on it. Since I considered them tastier than what we normally ate, the St. Lucy's day specials appealed to me. But my grandparents carried on as though they were making a sacrifice comparable to the saint's. The whole thing was supposed to insure healthy eyesight for us all in the year ahead. As far as I was concerned, St. Lucy's day also ushered in the Christmas season. On December 14, the day following the feast, I would set up a crèche on one of the trunks in the front room of the other house with Five and Ten Cent Store figures of the Holy Family, wise men, angels, and shepherds, arranged amid papier-mâché backgrounds of my own manufacture. Then I'd settle down to anticipate our Christmas Eve gala.

The Christmas Eve party was always held in the more luxurious surroundings on our side of the hall, though all the preparations were made in the other house. I particularly enjoyed the preparations, despite the near-certainty that I'd be suffering from my worst cold of the season by party time.

Neither my mother nor grandmother qualified as expert cooks and Pina was totally incompetent in the kitchen. Nevertheless, the traditional pastries had to be made. In our family, these had been originally of three varieties. But by the time I was old enough to know what was going on, *li cassateddi* had been relegated to the realm of legend.

"Remember when we used to make *li cassateddi?*" Pina would say.

"Ah, *li cassateddi,*" my mother would nod in awe.

"They were something," Vinnie always agreed.

Pina would drool at the thought. "Weren't they good?"

"Too heavy though," my mother remembered.

"Sometimes they were too heavy," my grandmother corrected, "not when I made them."

"What were they?" I'd ask.

Opinions varied.

"*Li cassateddi?* They were little things with cream in them."

"No. *Li cassateddi? Li cassateddi* had no cream in them. *La cassata* had cream, not *li cassateddi.*"

"But *li cassateddi* had cream in them too."

"Not exactly cream."

"Not when I made them."

"But they were good."

"Weren't they something? Why don't we make some now?"

"Ai, we don't have all the ingredients."

"And who is capable of doing all that work any more?"

"But they were worth it, weren't they?"

"Ahh. *Li cassateddi.*"

"*Li cassateddi.*"

All that was made in my time were *li sfingi* and *la pignolata.*

Li sfingi were oily, lumpy doughnuts without holes. They were supposed to be round, I guess. Perhaps they were even supposed to have holes. But although my grandmother kept plopping approximately the same size pieces of dough into a pot, with more or less the same wrist motion, no two *sfingi* ever came out alike. After they were cooked, they were stacked on a large platter—a tangled mass of angles and protuberances.

"Eat some now, Tommy, before I cover them," my grandmother recommended. "They are best when they are hot."

"But not too many," cautioned my mother.

Li sfingi were eaten after dunking them into a mound of granulated sugar. I did enjoy them hot, but I also liked eating the leftovers one or two days after Christmas, when they would sink into my digestive tract with a thud.

I liked *la pignolata* even better, because I had been allowed to help make it. The dough had to be rolled into long, thin strands, which were then cut into three-quarter-inch lengths. I was the dough-roller, my mother did the cutting, and my grandmother tossed the pieces into a frying pan. In the days of *li cassateddi*, it was said, the pan was an inch deep with honey, but in my day it was thinly lined with melted sugar. Then the fried pieces were dumped onto another platter where they stuck together and were sprinkled with colored sugar. Within minutes, *la pignolata* had changed from a gooey brown mass into a miniature Gibraltar. It took strong hands and a strong knife to hack off a piece of *pignolata* at our Christmas party, and strong teeth to eat it. I lacked all three, so I relied on my grandmother to cut me a piece and on my powers of salivation for the softening which had to precede my bite with the "good" molars on the right side of my mouth. I enjoyed it very much and considered myself lucky if I did not wind up with a toothache.

Since Catholics were not permitted to eat meat on the vigil of Christmas, the main course of our Christmas feast was sea food. There had always been several kinds of fish. After Nick's wife, Concetta, joined the family, there were even more varieties. They came from her father's fish store and they were free. There were sole and flounder fillets, shrimp, eels, squid, even lobster. This last creature was something which only my father had ever known existed. But the fish that really meant Christmas was *lu baccalaru* [codfish]. In prior years my grandfather had reserved the preparation of *lu baccalaru* to himself, according to his secret recipe. This custom had gone the way of *li cassateddi* and was recalled with equal admiration, even by my grandmother, who had to admit that her husband's *baccalaru* had been tasty indeed. This admission was met invariably with amusement since, for Sicilians, *"baccalaru"* was a word with connotations of genitalia.

Now it was Concetta who cooked *lu baccalaru*, and all the other fish. She'd arrive about five o'clock to take over the kitchen and overwhelm us with loud Neapolitan efficiency. While she cooked, my mother and grandmother, their pastry-making completed, began preparations on the spaghetti and vegetables. Broccoli and artichokes were always included. We were usually ready to start about nine o'clock, when my father would arrive from Newark, having left work early.

By midnight, the floor of our kitchen would be covered with wrapping paper from the presents we'd exchanged after eating. But long before that, about the time the *baccalaru* was being served, in fact, my grandmother had observed, "And so the feast is over. The ancients said, *After Christmas, the cold and famine.*"

The feast was over for us by Easter morning, too, but my mother and I had spent more time in church during the preceding three days than during all the rest of the year. "In Camporeale, I was never out of church during Holy Week," my mother used to say in explanation. Except in Holy Week, neither of us went to church except to see weddings on Sunday afternoons. The only one in the family who went to Mass regularly was my grandmother.

But she shared the attitude of the ancients who had said, *Priests and nuns—see their Mass and crack their ribs.*

Naturally, it was my grandmother who began our Easter season when she returned from Our Lady of Mount Carmel on Palm Sunday carrying a large quantity of fronds and complaining that they had passed out small thin stalks this year. Then she would tell how she'd managed to bring home such large fat ones.

"I went into the sacristy after Mass and said to the priest, 'Eh, look. Are these all the palms a faithful daughter of Mary is entitled to? Some people come to church to get baptized, married, buried, and get palms. Am I to be treated less well than they? They all grabbed more than I did. Because I am frail and old, because I do not push, I get cheated. Is this how the meek shall inherit the earth— getting robbed in the very house of the Virgin?'

"And the priest looked very upset and said, 'Calm yourself, dear lady. You are absolutely right. I am mortified that you should suffer this affront. Please accept my deepest apologies and these palms. Please forgive us poor servants of the Virgin.' And he handed me these."

My grandmother would conclude triumphantly, flinging the palms onto the kitchen table. This was my signal to begin weaving them into little crosses. I was the only one in the family who had learned the technique from my grandfather, who despite a complete lack of piety, knew how to make a mean cross. Neither my grandmother nor my mother could make them hold together, let alone loop and weave them into the intricate designs I made. To my grandfather's basic method, I had added the use of pins, making possible more curlicues and embellishments. I usually had enough palms to make two crosses for every room in both houses. They'd be looped over bedposts, placed on bureaus, and hung on nails from the walls. The old ones were never desecrated by throwing them into a garbage bag. They were burned in the pot-bellied stove.

On Holy Thursday night, my mother and I began our church-going by accompanying my grandmother to three of them. My grandmother said that in the old days she had visited nine churches, and had heard, though did not believe, that some people actually visited twelve or fifteen. Neither she nor my mother was clear about the purpose of these visits, saying simply that we were going to *li sipulchri*. To my recurring question about why we visited "sepulchers" the night before Christ was to be crucified, my grandmother answered, "Because Christ is in jail this night"; or "Because Christ is being shown on Pilate's balcony this night"; or "Because He is praying and sweating blood in the Garden of Gethsemane."

Whatever the reason for *li sipulchri*, the churches were beautifully decorated with flowers and shiny fabrics. We would begin by walking to 110th Street, to the Church of St. Anne, near the East Harlem gas tanks, structures which never failed to impress us and evoke some comment from my mother such as "Madonna, how large is America." We thought of the neighborhood around St. Anne's as poorer than ours, and of the church as a ramshackle institution struggling for survival. "Still, they do their best to put up a good sepulcher," my grandmother said.

After St. Anne's, we went to the Church of Our Lady

Queen of Angels, on 113th Street. This was an "American" church, because none of the sermons were in Italian, but it was, nonetheless, Catholic, my grandmother assured us. It was the smallest of the three churches we visited, the third, of course, being Our Lady of Mount Carmel.

In all the churches, the procedure was the same. The faithful filed down a side aisle to the altar, genuflected, dropped some money into a basket, and, for the most part, proceeded up the other side aisle and out of the church. A few, including the three of us, did not leave immediately, but walked up the center aisle and into a pew, to pray. In each church, my grandmother said her rosary in a sibilant whisper, sitting on the edge of the pew, as close as she could come to kneeling, while my mother sat quietly. I would kneel for a couple of minutes and would then sit back to watch the people filing past. Everybody in East Harlem, young and old, seemed to make the tour of *li sipulchri*. The shuffling feet and jingling coins filled me with sorrow that Our Lord, in the garden, on the balcony, or in jail, would soon be killed.

Other feelings also stirred in me on our pilgrimage to *li sipulchri*. The faint suggestion of spring that was in the air on those Holy Thursday nights, the sight of all the boys and girls my age on the streets, going from church to church unaccompanied by their elders, both exhilarated and depressed me. I imagined myself to be one of the boys, shouting, and having a good time, feeling the girls and having them like it. Or I would walk a little bit ahead of my mother and grandmother, pretending not to be with them, trying to look the bored and sophisticated lone wolf, wanting a girl to notice me and yet dreading the prospect. But I knew it was all a ridiculous fantasy, that nothing would ever happen to me in a million years of visiting *li sipulchri.*

The next Easter ceremony was one my mother and I performed alone on Good Friday morning—going to Our Lady of Mount Carmel to kiss the feet of Jesus. All the flowers of the night before had disappeared, and there would be only a few elderly women in the church. The statues of saints, draped in purple since the beginning of Lent, once more dominated the scene. The center gate of the altar rail was open, and resting on the marble steps, there was a dark-brown wooden cross, about four feet high, with an effigy of Christ nailed to it. A nun knelt by it, holding a napkin, with which she wiped Christ's feet after each kiss. The feet were waxy, with freshly repainted bright red trickles on the insteps where a single nail pierced them both. I followed my mother in the ritual, mindful of her advice: "You don't have to actually touch your lips to the feet."

After lunch we'd return for "the three hours of agony," commemorating in song and sermon the time Christ spent hanging from the cross, and after dinner we'd go back again, with my grandmother, for the Stations of the Cross in Italian. All the priests of Mount Carmel participated in this rite, parading slowly around the church and pausing before each of the fourteen Stations depicted on its walls. At each stop, the congregation rose, faced in the direction of the Station, and repeated aloud the appropriate

76

prayers. My mother was silent on all but the Our Fathers and Hail Marys, and I was silent even for these, not knowing them in Italian. My grandmother knew all the prayers, and recited them in an emotion-choked voice.

On Holy Saturday morning, my mother and I made our final visit to church, to see the Risen Saviour.

When I told her that Christ was not supposed to rise from the dead until Easter Sunday, she assured me that in Camporeale Christ always came back to life at noon on Holy Saturday. That was the time when all the bells in town would start ringing.

"I don't understand that," I said. "It's a mistake."

"It's no mistake. They had the true religion in Camporeale."

Apparently they had the true religion in Naples too, because when we got to Our Lady of Mount Carmel, about 11:30 or so, a small statue of the Risen Saviour was already on display over the main altar. Despite the glad tidings thus signified, there were even fewer people attending than on Good Friday morning. My mother and I would sit in the front center pew until noon, when the church bell rang, and then go home.

The following day, my grandmother was the only one who went to Mass, just as on any other Sunday.

We paid almost no attention to American holidays like The Day of the Dead [Memorial Day], *Lu Forte Gelato* [the Fourth of July], or The Day of the Chicken [Thanksgiving Day]. The only notice of them would be taken by my mother should I happen to have a headache, a toothache, or some other complaint during those days. In such

77

cases, she would repeat what she always said at least once during our observances of the important holidays of Our Lady of Mount Carmel, St. Lucy's Day, Christmas, and Easter: *"God deliver us from His feasts."*

THE UNCLES

The evening my uncle Nick came to the other house to announce the birth of his first-born son, Vinnie was on our side of the hall listening to the radio and my grandmother, my mother, and I were in Jefferson Park. This acre of greenery by the East River often attracted us on warm evenings when my grandmother had no cutaways from *Li Roggispiti* to sew. We always sat on the same bench, remaining there until my mother suffered her first mosquito bite, at which point we would rise agitatedly and start to walk home. Our regular habits had attracted the attention of an old lady whom my grandmother had nicknamed *La Confettara* because she always seemed to be sucking a confection, although she was probably just sucking her gums. Every time *La Confettara* passed our bench, she would shake her head and exclaim in wet Neapolitan, "There they sit: St. Anne, the Virgin Mary, and the Christ Child, all three in the stable. Why don't they get up and walk about as I do? I could never sit in one place. I must be up and moving, seeing what's going on, not sitting in the same stable."

"This is our pleasure, to sit in our stable," my grand-mother would call back. "Some people walk, others sit. Eventually we will all lie down forever. You first, dear lady."

Perhaps the mosquitoes were extraordinarily quiet that evening, or *La Confettara* had so annoyed my grandmother that we sat on the bench longer than usual, just to spite her. Whatever the reason, by the time we got home, all was quiet except for my grandfather's snores. We did not hear about Nick and Concetta's baby until the following morning. And we never heard the full story of what had happened when Nick had given the great news to my grandfather.

I knew that relations between the old man and his younger son had been strained for many years, because of Nick's criminal record. The details of that were obscure, consisting only of my grandmother's yearly reminiscences of how her heart had been broken on a day in court long ago, when she'd heard her son sentenced to a year in the *riformatorio*. Pina thought the sentence had had to do with the robbery of a jewelry store in which Nick had participated with two other youths. My mother believed the crime had consisted of inadvertently receiving stolen property. The only thing clear was that Nick's indiscretion had angered his father tremendously. Thereafter he always referred to his son as *lu galiotu* (the jailbird). Evidently, he had behaved damnably when *lu galiotu* told him of the blessed event. At any rate, Nick had charged headlong from the other house into the corridors of officialdom to have the baby's birth certificate changed. No longer was he Thomas Tarantola, in honor of his grandfather. He became Nicholas Tarantola, Junior.

There was general consternation when we heard the news.

To my grandmother it made no sense. "*Giugnio*, what kind of name is that? Why not call him *Agosto*? If he's going to be named after a month, it might as well be the month he was born in."

"Nick says *Giugnio* means the baby is named for the father," my mother explained.

"Whoever heard of naming a baby for his father? Besides, his father's name is Nicola, not *Giugnio*."

"The baby's name is Nicola, too. Nick. Junior means 'the Second.' Nicholas Tarantola, the Second," Vinnie said.

"There have been plenty of Nicholas Tarantolas in the family, not just two," said my grandmother, "but never one after another like this. It's not the way Christians behave. Ah well, who knows what Carnival Face must have said to my son to make him change the birth certificate. If only I had been at home instead of in that stable, I could have kept Carnival Face in line, and my grandson would have been named in a fit Christian way. First the oldest son marries a savage. Barbara, *barbara*—aptly named, a barbarian who doesn't understand Italian and doesn't believe in the saints. And now this. All the fault of that man. Sleep, Carnival Face. Snore your head off on that cot. Choke to death on your snoring."

My grandmother ended her tirade with a thunderous

passing of wind. "Take that, Carnival Face," she said. "I shit in your eyes."

Carnival Face never spoke to his younger son again. Nick, despite his precipitous action, was not one to hold a grudge. But when he'd come to visit, my grandfather would retire to his cot, if he wasn't already there, cursing the rest of us for not turning our backs too. As Nick's visits became less frequent, my grandmother began stopping by his apartment Sunday mornings on her way back from Mass.

After one such occasion, she reported that Junior's left ear seemed somewhat larger than his right ear. My grandfather emerged from his room, nodding righteously. "All of you," he said, "will come to bad ends."

"Go to sleep, stupid," his wife shouted. "Are you satisfied now that my grandson is a marked man? It is your doing. You cursed him."

The old man looked satisfied and returned to his cot.

The whole matter came to a head that Christmas Eve.

By the time my father arrived from Newark bearing the presents he always bought at the last minute, the men of the family were assembled in the kitchen on our side of the hall, looking at the presents already resting under the artificial tree I'd decorated. The women were still in the kitchen of the other house, preparing to carry in the food. My grandfather was still on his cot.

My father began the festivities by pouring full shots of whiskey for Uncle Nick, Uncle Charlie, and himself, half a shot for Vinnie, and small amounts for me and for Uncle Charlie's son, Thomas Kenneth. After we'd toasted the occasion and established that time sure did fly, my father asked if anyone had read what LaGuardia had said about the tinhorns.

"What read?" said Uncle Charlie. "Why should I read what that Sheeny says?" He pronounced the last word with a long *a*.

"What do you mean 'Sheeny'?" my father asked, as Barbara appeared with a hot kettle, closely followed by Pina, Concetta, my mother, and my grandmother, all heavily laden.

Charlie ignored the question, switching to Sicilian to ask his mother where his father was.

She told him that he was snoring and, looking at Nick and then again at Charlie, she added, "He wouldn't come. He's always on that pigsty of a cot, anyhow."

Barbara put her kettle down with annoyance. She was annoyed whenever her husband spoke Sicilian.

"I get it," Charlie said, going back to English, "because of this jerk over here." He thrust his balding head in Nick's direction, without looking at him. Nick said nothing.

My father was not to be distracted. "LaGuardia is Italian. What do you mean 'Sheeny'?"

"Go wan, he's a phony Sheeny bastid," Charlie said, "and you jerks voted for him. Serves you right."

"Serves us right? Don't you think he's a good mayor? He's chasing out the crooks."

"He's a phony like everybody else. We even got phonies and Sheenies right in the family now."

"I think LaGuardia is part Jew and part Wop," Nick said with a strained chuckle.

Charlie changed the subject abruptly. "But what about this kid here?" He was looking at me. I felt myself flush and not from my cold, which hadn't been such a bad one that year.

"Tommy? What about him?" my father wanted to know.

"What does he do all day?"

"He goes to school. What should he do, work as an apprentice blacksmith, like in the old country?"

"You don't get what I mean. I mean after school. He don't go out. He don't play on the street. He got no friends. He just mopes here all day, right? Is that all he does, just stay here and read and write? No wonder he gets sick. No wonder he needs glasses. Me, I'm forty, you see me with glasses? You see *my* Tommy with glasses? He has a good time. That's all he cares about. Look at his red cheeks. He's three years younger than this kid here and he's already bigger."

I looked up to observe my healthy cousin, who was hovering around the presents, trying to decipher the labels. I always looked forward to his visits. We played cops and robbers or cowboys and Indians in the "Now you must shoot me and I must be hurt and you must try to run away, then I must trip you" tradition. There'd be no time to play that night, though. After the meal I had to read the tags on the presents, "To Nick from Concetta," "To Concetta from Barbara," "To Barbara from Concetta," and hand them out. Someone was sure to compliment me on my reading ability, and someone else would undoubtedly point out that my brother, Vinnie, was smart too. The two of us would do the family proud some day.

84

Then Charlie started asking me direct questions. "Hey, Tommy, what do you do all day, kid?" He had assumed a jovially avuncular manner. "Why don't you go on the street? What's the matter, kid?"

"Nothing," I said. "I like it inside."

"Too much reading is no good for you. Makes you crazy."

But it makes me the best presenter of presents, I thought, noticing that my uncle was about to lose interest in his nephew's social adjustment.

"Is there any wine?" Charlie asked. "Anybody bring wine?"

"You want another shot?" my father inquired, raising his right shoulder.

"I said wine."

"We must have some wine. *Santa, vino ci ne?*"

Concetta told my mother not to bother because they'd brought some. "Nicky, where'd you put it?"

"Forget it," Charlie said. "Remember *Cavalleria Rusticana*? I don't want your wine, *Cumpari Turiddu*, it would turn to poison in my stomach. And what do you think? That I don't know about opera? The greatest operas were by Sicilians. I hear this Verdi was a Sicilian."

Nick shrugged. Concetta glared.

"First place," my father said, "Verdi didn't write *Cavalleria Rusticana*. It was Mascagni and I don't think *he* was Sicilian, let alone Verdi. Second place, you know as much about opera as I know about medicine. Third place, what the hell do you need wine for? I thought you were a Canadian Club drinker. We got three bottles plus scotch, bourbon, and rye."

85

Charlie grunted angrily, grabbed a bottle of the Canadian Club, opened the front door, and walked out. "Now where the hell did he go?" my father wondered. "We're almost ready to eat."

"Come on, everybody sit down," my grandmother commanded. After chairs had been scraped and shuffled, and all were seated, Pina asked what it was the ancients used to say on occasions like these. *"Mille di questi giorni,"* my father replied. *"May there be a thousand such days."*

"But why," he continued, "must we have pasta even on these days? Who can eat all the fish if we fill up on this first?"

My grandmother assured him that a meal without pasta was no meal at all.

"You will be surprised to hear, then, that many Americans never eat pasta at all," my father told her. "Isn't that right, Barbara? Did you ever eat macaroni in Georgia?"

"Only aig noodles, sometahm," Barbara answered, delighted at being brought into the conversation. For the next few minutes she talked animatedly with my father in English, while Concetta talked with her customary vigor, in Neapolitan, to my mother and grandmother, and Nick, Pina, Vinnie, Thomas Kenneth, and I ate in silence. I knew that I would be enjoined from eating most of the varieties of fish by my mother's looks which said, "No, bad for your stomach," so I had to fill up on macaroni. To that end, my mother had put more on my plate than on any of the others.

I was about three-quarters of the way through it when Uncle Charlie reappeared.

"Where y'all been, stranger?" his wife asked cheerily. "Yew pasta gittin cold."

"I've been visiting the old man. He's entitled to celebrate Christmas, too."

"Why don't he come on in heah, then?"

"Leave him alone. I'll keep him company." Charlie hissed this in his best movie tough-guy style. Like Aunt Pina, he was an admirer of George Raft. By his own account, one of the big moments of his life had come when he'd seen George Raft walking toward him on a downtown street. The actor had been staring intently at him, and Charlie recalled thinking, "But what does this guy want?" Then, six months later, Charlie went to see Raft's latest movie and the mystery was solved. George was wearing the same suit on screen that my uncle had been wearing that day on the street. George Raft knew class when he saw it.

Charlie made good his promise to keep his father company. He gobbled his pasta and retreated across the hall, returning to the festive board in time to down a few shrimp, before going back to the other house. He kept shuttling that way throughout most of the long meal, but by the time *la pignolata* was being hacked at, he seemed to have disappeared for good.

While the dishes were being cleared, I caught Thomas Kenneth's eye and he bounded from his chair to my side.

"You want to play cops and robbers?" I said.

"Let's open the presents. Start reading the tags."

"Tommy." My grandmother turned from the plate-filled sink to address me. "Go ask your uncle if he wants coffee."

"Me?"

"No, not you. Leonardo DaVinci."

"Come on, Tommy," I said to my cousin. "Let's go in the other house."

"Let's open the presents."

"Okay, but before we can open them we have to go to the other house to get your father."

He ran out and was pounding on the door before I was off my chair. I got there in time to join him in calling "Tommy" in answer to my grandfather's thick "*Cu e docu?*" and Charlie's boisterous "Who's 'at?" It took my uncle a long time to open the door. They had bolted all four locks.

"Grandma wants to know if you want coffee." Since I spoke in English, I was obviously addressing Charlie, but I was looking at my grandfather. He was sitting on the kitchen table, wearing his cap and swinging his legs like a child.

"Yeh, yeh, we'll be in in a little while," Charlie said, sounding positively gleeful. In Sicilian, he asked his father if he'd care to dance again.

"*Beh,*" said my grandfather. "Let's do a *tarantedda*, a Tarantola *tarantedda*." He slid down from the table, Charlie grabbed his arm, and the two of them began spinning around. My grandfather sang a song called *Principale Vossia Lu Sape*, about a long-downtrodden employee who confronts his employer with an ultimatum: "Boss, you know it. If you don't give me my week's pay, I won't be back Monday."

88

Charlie accompanied him with la-la-las and shrieks of laughter.

I watched them in bewilderment, a little frightened. Thomas Kenneth seemed unsure whether to join the dance or start crying.

"Yeh, yeh, I'll come over for coffee as soon as we finish this dance," Charlie said, stumbling close to us. "Soon as we finish the Tarantola *tarantedda*. Ho-ho-hee-hee-la-la-la."

Thomas Kenneth and I retreated next door, where the party was much quieter.

"Did you tell him?" my grandmother wanted to know.

"Yes," I said, "he's coming."

"What are they doing in there?"

"They're dancing," I said.

"Dancing? Something is going to happen, something calamitous. Carnival Face hasn't danced in forty years."

My grandmother didn't have long to wait. In a few minutes, Charlie appeared, reeling as though he were still doing the *tarantedda*, and carrying the empty whiskey bottle. "We need more Canadian Club," he said.

"You need some coffee," my father told him.

"Oh yeah, coffee. Is this jerk over here having coffee too?" He made the same motion with his head that he'd made toward Nick earlier in the evening. This time his brother did not remain silent.

"Why are you calling me a jerk?" he demanded.

Charlie hesitated long enough for my father to interrupt with his favorite joke, the one about Neal Dunn, an Irish immigrant who came to America and forgot all about his dear old mother. He hadn't written her in three years. So when neighbor lad Sean O'Shamus was going to leave for America too, old lady Dunn asked him to look up her son who, she was sure, by that time must have made it to the White House. As soon as he got off the boat, Sean stepped into a saloon and asked the bartender where the White House was. The bartender motioned to the men's room. Sean stormed back there and saw a pair of feet under the closed door of a booth. "Hey," Sean hollered, "you Nealy Dunn?" "Yes," came the timorous reply. "Then why the bejesus don't you write to your mother?"

But Uncle Charlie was not to be put off. The joke only gave him more ammunition. "That's all this jerk over here is good for, taking a crap," he said.

"I asked you why you are calling me a jerk," Nick said evenly.

"I am calling you a jerk because you *are* a jerk. By what right did you break the family tradition?"

"What tradition?"

"What *right* did you have to break the family tradition?"

"I can hear you. Can you hear me? What tradition?"

"The family tradition of calling my son Tommy after our father, and this kid Tommy after our father, and *your* kid Tommy after our father. You broke that chain. You dishonored the old man. You acted like a jerk and a prick."

"I don't have to answer to you for anything," Nick said. "But I don't like being called a jerk and a prick."

"You don't like it? Too bad, because that's what you are, a jerk and a prick."

"Maybe you want to settle this outside," Nick said, rising casually from his chair.

My mother, my grandmother, Concetta, and Pina were all trying to restore calm by yelling incoherently. My father's voice rose above the din to shout, "Merry Christmas! Merry Christmas! Let's open the presents." Barbara stood quietly in a corner of the kitchen, not doing a thing.

Nick had his hand on the doorknob when Charlie threw the empty Canadian Club bottle at him. It flew past Nick and shattered in the bedroom. The women's screams grew louder, and they clutched their hands to the sides of their heads. In the confusion, Nick let go of the doorknob, walked calmly up to Charlie, and punched him squarely in the middle of his face. Charlie's nose began to bleed while my father put his arms around Nick, telling him to calm down and forget it because his brother was drunk. Nick assured him that he was perfectly calm. "Okay, okay, go inside then." My father nudged Nick past the broken bottle and up to the yellow curtain that held back the cold. "Okay, now stay there," my father said, returning to the kitchen where Charlie was nursing his nose and cursing his brother, surrounded by the screaming women, while Vinnie, Thomas Kenneth, and I walked nervously around the group, saying things like "That's enough, now, forget it, it's Christmas," all quite inaudibly.

Suddenly saying, "I'll kill him!" Charlie lurched to retrieve the broken top of the bottle. Before he could advance on Nick, all of us except Barbara had grabbed a piece of Charlie or of one another, pulling and hauling him back to the kitchen.

"Lemme go, lemme go. I'll kill him." Over and over Charlie yelled it, waving the broken glass high over his head, while we held him, dragging him farther and farther into the kitchen, knocking over the tree and stepping all over the presents. It went on for five or ten minutes—Nick standing quietly in the shadows by the yellow curtain, and the rest of us in the kitchen, hanging on to Charlie and hollering. When Thomas Kenneth and I began to cry, it seemed the cue for all to turn their entreaties toward Nick. "Go home, Nick, go home!" we shouted and sobbed, in both English and Sicilian. His wife's voice rose over the rest. "Go home, Nick. I'll meet you home."

"If he wants to fight me, let him fight," Nick said.

"No, no. Go home, Nick, go home."

Acting just as calmly as he had all night, Nick walked toward us, stirring Charlie, who had gone almost limp under our mass holding operation, into a new frenzy. We had all we could do not to lose him.

"Okay, I'm going home," Nick said. "Merry Christmas."

We still held on to Charlie while he ranted, "He ran away. He's afraid of me. You let him go. I would have killed him."

There was more tugging and pulling before we could relax. Finally, there came a moment of total silence, broken by Barbara.

"Y'all can let go of him now."

After we drank more coffee, not saying much, Barbara gathered up the presents tagged for Charlie, Thomas Kenneth, and herself, and did her best to repair the damage to the tree. She then wiped her husband's face, while Thomas Kenneth asked if he could open his presents.

"We'll do it at home, honey," she said. Charlie seemed sober when they left.

Concetta left soon after, carrying her presents, and Nick's, and Junior's. My grandmother and Pina returned to the other house where, they later reported, they found my grandfather snoring on his cot.

I didn't open my presents until Christmas morning, the first and only time I ever waited that long. I got a big water-color set from Concetta and Nick.

My grandfather had been dead for a year when Concetta and Nick's second child, Vickie, was born. She was baptized Vittoria, in honor of my grandmother, Vittoria Tarantola.

THE ALIENS

After we'd finished eating on Sunday afternoons, my mother washed the linoleum in our house. In warm weather, she started in the front room. In cold weather, when the front room was sealed off behind the yellow curtain, she started in her bedroom. I would remain in the kitchen, listening to the radio, until she'd arrive there with her mop and soapy water, at which point I'd retreat to the other house. I was about to do just that one Sunday, when the announcer broke into the broadcast of the Giant football game to say that Japanese planes had bombed Pearl Harbor. I translated the bulletin for my mother, explaining that *Pelle Abbo* belonged to the United States. Even so, she seemed unaware of the import of the event. Years later, though, she told me how she'd felt at that moment. "My legs went numb, and then my arms. I thought of your brother and asked the Virgin to protect him. Then I cursed your father for bringing that instrument into the house." She meant the radio.

She acted calm at the time. Nor, for that matter, was I immediately upset by the news. Not until Vinnie came

94

home from the movies that evening looking worried did I begin to realize World War II might have an impact on our family.

The war's first effect was on my grandparents and my mother. Two months after Pearl Harbor, they had to register as enemy aliens.

Vinnie and I, ready to act as interpreters, accompanied them to the registration place, the basement of a school on 119th Street which Pina had attended. The evening was a snowy one, leading to a dispute on the way between my mother and grandmother about what the snow portended. In their excitement, they'd forgotten whether rain was a good omen and snow an evil one, or vice versa. Finally, my grandfather turned angrily toward his wife, nearly losing his footing.

"Be quiet, evil woman," he said. "Here we are on our way to jail and you blabber about these stupidities."

"No one is going to arrest you," my grandmother answered, "though they should. If you had become a citizen when you came here, as Santina's husband did, we would not be going through this night. Instead you started a shuttle service between Ellis Island and Palermo."

"A citizen of this whore's paradise? I'd rather rot in jail first. Your precious son-in-law, the American citizen, where is he? You see what turning American means? He should be here by his wife's side and by ours, protecting us from this inquisition, but I do not see him."

"He is working," my grandmother replied. "Something you wouldn't understand."

"And your two sons, where are they? I do not see them.

All we have are my two grandsons. But it is just as well. I am afraid of no one. When I go into this place tonight, I will raise my hand high and say, 'Viva Mussolini, abassu l'America.' And don't try to hold me back, buttana."

"I wouldn't think of it. Perhaps they will arrest you."

"If so, I will be detained for only a few weeks. America will soon be part of Italy. I have seen it in the newspapers."

My grandmother laughed uproariously. "Newspapers? And when did you learn to read?"

"I understand the photographs. I have been looking at them with my two grandsons. They show me pictures of people they say are American generals and commanders, and they all look like vegetable mongers."

It was true. The pictures the Daily News printed in those days all seemed to have been taken when our military leaders were out of uniform.

"No hat, no buttons, no insignia of any kind," my grandfather continued. "Even a corporal in our cavalry looked better than that. These ice-cream eaters don't even have mustaches. When I was in the cavalry, my mustache was black and ferocious, and I waxed it every night."

"And after four years of waxing your mustache, they promoted you to appuntatu [private first class]. Such was your ferocity. You rivaled Napoleon Bonaparte." My grandmother was still laughing.

"Silence, sow! Mussolini will bring them all to their knees. After all, he is Sicilian."

"Idiot. Mussolini is no Sicilian. He is from northern Italy."

"It doesn't matter what you say. He is the son of a blacksmith, as I am."

We had arrived at the school. My grandfather raised his right hand high in the air and shouted, *"Vittoria al'Italia!"* Then he followed the rest of us into the basement. Inside he submitted meekly to being photographed and to having his index finger smeared and rolled onto a sheet of paper. He nodded vigorously at the questions of the examining clerk which Vinnie answered for him.

Outside in the snow again, it was my grandmother's turn to be irate. "And so we discovered America," she said. "This is the land where the President serves frankfurters and beans to the royal house of England. *Presidente Rosa Verde*, the Green Rose who pricks us with his thorns. In the land discovered by an Italian, the Green Rose now brands us enemies and traitors. The real traitor was Cristoforo Colombo, the *facchino* from *l'alta Italia*. Cristoforo Colombo should have had a hemorrhage before he set sail for these Godforsaken shores."

My mother merely urged me to wrap my scarf more securely around my neck and checked to see that the earflaps of my cap were properly positioned.

A few days later, we received three pink alien registration booklets in the mail. I still have my mother's. I keep it because of the photograph inside. The way her hair looks, dark and neat, you might not guess that it's gathered in a bun at the back. Her face is unlined, her eyes are alert, and, surprisingly, there is a hint that her thin lips might have broken out into a smile after the ordeal of picture-taking ended. It must be the best photograph ever taken of her.

Her signature, however, which runs from bottom to top on the left side of the picture and spills over onto the page, betrays the emotion of that night. To the left of it is her "right index fingerprint." The name Santina Martana appears in two other places on the page: in a second, equally shaky signature at the bottom and, written by a different, official hand, at the top along with the "Alien Registration Number 4045148."

The facing page contains the following information: "Birth date: Oct. 10, 1899. Born in or near: Camporeale Trapani, Italy. Citizen or subject of: Italy. Length of residence in United States: 22 yrs., 2 mos. Address of residence: 223 East 117th St., New York, N.Y. Height: 5 ft., 4 in. Weight: 114 lbs. Color of hair: black. Distinctive marks: none." Next to these specifications appears the imprint of a rubber stamp, a little larger than a postmark. It reads, "New York, N.Y. M.O.B. Feb. 17, 1942." At the bottom of the page is the notice, "Application filed in Alien Registration Division. Copy filed with Federal Bureau of Investigation office at New York, N.Y."

In the spring, there was another piece of government mail in the Martana mailbox. It was a letter containing "Greetings" for my brother Vinnie from the Green Rose.

Seven nights a week I wrote a four-page letter to Vinnie on a sheet of my typewriter paper folded in half. Since my brother could not read Italian, the first page was a translation of my mother's dictation and always read pretty much the same.

"Dear son, I am fine and hope to hear the same from you. I was glad to receive your last letter. I understand it is very hot in Fort Breckinridge, Kentucky. The weather here has not been too bad. I am getting things ready for the next gift package I will send you. If there is anything special you need, please let me know. Well, that's about all for now. Hugs and kisses from your grandfather, your grandmother, your uncle Charlie and family, your uncle Nick and family, and your aunt Pina. Your father sends his love and will write to you in English on his day off. Write soon. God protect you. Once more I send you love from everybody, especially from your brother and from Your Loving Mother."

The three other pages, the ones from me, I wrote in a far smaller hand. They included an expanded version of *The Daily Bugle*, which I crammed with sports results and war bulletins, as if Fort Breckinridge were cut off from all communication with the outside world. Then there was the home news.

I let Vinnie know that he'd been placed under the protection of Our Lady of Mount Carmel in two places. A committee of devout and patriotic residents of our block had erected a shrine to Our Lady in a vacant lot near the corner of Second Avenue. They'd bought a little statue of her enclosed in a glass dome and put it between two wooden panels on which were lettered the names of all the service men from 117th Street between Second and Third avenues. Votive candles were kept lit before the shrine day and night. My mother and I stopped there at least once a day on our way to and from school to drop a quarter into a slot cut into the statue's pedestal and think prayerful thoughts of safe homecoming. In addition, I told Vinnie, his name had been lettered in the Church of Our Lady of Mount Carmel itself, the basement of which had been converted into The Victory Chapel. On The Victory Chapel's front wall was a hastily painted mural showing the Madonna surrounded by members of the Army, Navy, Marines, and Coast Guard beseeching her assistance. On the side walls were hundreds of names. My mother had donated five dollars to have Vinnie's among them.

I wrote to my brother of how I missed the thrill of athletic competition in the Saturday baseball games with him, and about the way I'd been practicing in anticipation of his return. I'd had my mother buy me a bigger bat, almost two feet long. As a consequence of the wartime paper shortage and because I needed the typewriter paper for the letters to him, I used only one sheet of it in making the baseballs, for the outer wrapper, and newspaper for the core. The ball thus produced was deader, as in Ty Cobb's day. Nevertheless, I grew proficient. I slapped singles, cracked doubles, and blasted home runs into the kitchen. Once I even hit a triple. I grew lyrical describing the ball's trajectory to the kitchen window sill, its bounce onto the fire escape, and the way it stayed there, miraculously not falling into Filippo's yard. I reminded my brother, in all humility, that not even he had ever accomplished such a feat.

I told him that the other house was now not only

Yankee Stadium but Madison Square Garden as well. I
had bent a wire clothes hanger into a roughly circular shape
and slid its hook into the crack over the front-room door.
I made basketballs by stuffing great gobs of newspaper
into brown paper bags and tying them up. I had become
an all-around athlete, I said, able to sink dozens of foul
shots in a row.

Vinnie's replies were usually short, addressed solely to
my mother, and nearly as cut and dried as her own "letters." I translated them into Sicilian for her. Occasionally
he would write a longer one, a few of them directed to me,
in which he expounded on the food, the marches, his
buddies, twenty-four-hour passes in Evansville, Indiana,
and weekend ones in Terre Haute.

I didn't know what my father wrote Vinnie in his weekly
letters, so I frequently included some of the stories he'd
told Uncle Nick or Uncle Charlie. (After their fight, my
uncles visited separately, on alternate Monday nights.)
Though I was as shy and nervous as ever around my father,
I enjoyed hearing him tell stories on himself, provided he
wasn't looking at me, and I knew Vinnie had enjoyed
them too. They fell into two main groups; those about his
New Orleans days, generally retold at my uncle Charlie's
request, and all of which Vinnie already knew, and waiter
stories, of which there seemed to be a never ending new
supply. My father had been made headwaiter of Kreiner's
Restaurant, and shortly after that an incident happened
that added to his repertoire. I relayed it to my brother. A
drunken customer, on his way out of the restaurant on a
rainy day, demanded to see the headwaiter.

"I am the headwaiter, sir," my father informed him.

"Come on, quit your kidding and lemme see the head-waiter," the drunk said, pointing his umbrella.

My father assured him that he was looking at him, whereupon the drunk started laughing.

"I never seen such a shrimp headwaiter in all my life. You're all head. Where's the rest of you?"

My father recalled that he asked the man what his complaint was, "But this fella just kept laughing and insulting me. He was a big fella, over six feet. Not a regular customer."

When he'd stood enough ridicule, my father grabbed the umbrella while its owner was still bent low with laughter and brought it crashing down on his head, almost simultaneously biting his left ear. Then, summoning all his strength, my father grabbed him under his arms, dragged him to the door, and kicked him onto the wet sidewalk. Mr. Kreiner congratulated my father on the head-waiterly way in which he'd handled the situation.

Another story I reported to Vinnie concerned my father's new bifocals. He was having trouble getting used to them, so when he had to go to the pantry to get fresh linens, he said it was difficult for him to distinguish the tablecloths and napkins from the white-uniformed waitresses. "Especially Dottie's backside. It sure looks like a tablecloth to me, and I keep reaching for it all the time."

I wrote to Vinnie about how, since his departure, my mother listened to WOV, the Italian-language radio station, all day long, paying particular attention to the news programs. I rarely could make sense out of them, I said,

because the announcers declaimed the news in a rapid
stream of polysyllables which had no counterparts in
Sicilian. I doubted my mother understood much either,
but she seemed awe-struck by them, particularly when the
newscaster was one Guido Lupavelli, who doubled as a
disk jockey. More than once she remarked on the mascu-
linity of his voice, and on what a fine man he must be.

There were other radio personalities my mother liked,
foremost among them Diana Baldi, a kind of Italian Martha
Deane. Unlike that lady, however, Diana Baldi always in-
terviewed the same person, a furrier who was one of her
sponsors. I don't think her other sponsor, a salad oil manu-
facturer, the name of whose product translated as "Peace,
Oh My God," was ever on the program, but his product
was undoubtedly responsible for Miss Baldi's theme song.
It was Leonora's great aria from *La Forza Del Destino*,
"Pace, Pace Mio Dio." My mother could not afford a fur
coat, but Miss Baldi's convincing sales talk, coupled with
the impossibility of obtaining imported olive oil due to the
war, made her buy Peace, Oh My God. I wrote Vinnie that
she said she'd had no idea anything extracted from peanuts
could be so good.

But the most important programs on WOV were the
ones put on by the dramatic companies. The companies of
Mario Badolati "featuring Anna Calamai," and of Gino
Caimi "with Augusta Ciolli, premier actress," were my
mother's favorites. They put on serialized works, some
original and others adapted from literary classics like *I
Promessi Sposi* or from the lives of famous people like
Mother Cabrini. Each serial went on for three or four

months. A few weeks before its end, there would be a momentous announcement that the company was ready to perform the drama, in person and in its entirety, on the Italian theater circuit. For us, this meant the Triboro, a former burlesque house on 125th Street near Third Avenue.

There was nothing glamorous about accompanying my mother and grandmother to the Triboro. The performance started early on Sunday afternoon and went on into the evening. I told Vinnie that it seemed to me that out of an elapsed time of at least five hours, less than half was devoted to actual performing. The rest of the time, the curtain was down between acts. The play had twelve of them. After each one, tremendous hammering ensued behind the lowered curtain and continued until the audience became restive and began to clap. That would make the hammering grow louder and faster, assuring us that in a few minutes the curtain, *lu separio*, would rise again.

To see us through our long stay, my grandmother brought a shopping bag full of roast chicken and Italian bread. She kept it on her lap until we'd consumed its contents, because mice had been seen in the aisles of the Triboro.

In addition to the play, our Sunday at the theater included *un grande spettacolo di varieta* to begin the proceedings, and *una strepitosa farsa da ridere* to end them. The cast of the "great variety spectacle" consisted of Neapolitan singers like Clara Stella and Ria Rosa, whom I couldn't stand, singing their big radio hits. My own favorite WOV singer, a crooner named Ralph Pedi, never showed up on these bills, and everybody's favorite Italian popular singer of the time, Carlo Buti, had returned to Italy before the war, leaving only his phonograph records behind. Guido Lupavelli played them over and over on WOV. In his most notable record, "I Left My Heart on Broadway," Carlo Buti had made Broadway into a three syllable word with the stress on the last syllable: *"Ho lasciato il mio cor a Broduhweh."*

"The uproarious farce to laugh" at the end of the day was, of course, intended to leave the audience in this desirable condition. But the emotional drain of the play was usually too much for the comedians to overcome.

There were few men and no other children at the Triboro performances. I wondered about the feelings of those Italian ladies as they entered and left the theater. The lobby walls were still decorated with huge photographs of the performers hired by the theater's former lessees. Perhaps my mother and grandmother regarded the blown-up burlesque queens as "art," like the paintings of nudes in the Metropolitan Museum of Art which my godfather had once taken the family to see. In any case, I looked at the Triboro pictures surreptitiously, not taking any chances on reminding my mother of my confessed weakness for naked women.

When Vinnie wrote once that my letters were "pretty funny," it spurred me to greater efforts. I devoted a couple of letters to Old Stink Pants, the elderly Palermitan widow who had worked on cutaways with my grandmother years before. She had taken to dropping in on us Saturday mornings, never remembering that my grandmother was at work then. "And where is *la signora Vittoria* today?" she would ask. "Taking the morning air, like the noblewoman she is?"

When told of her visits, my grandmother would remind us that Old Stink Pants was a very well-educated woman. Though my mother and I saw little evidence of it, in deference to her cultural attainments, we always entertained her in the more dignified surroundings of our house. Her studies seemed limited to the plot of Verdi's *A Masked Ball*, which she never failed to recite in detail every time she visited us. We did learn, however, that she had been aptly nicknamed.

I was always restless in her presence. I had been taught that children should not absent themselves when there were visitors. But she kept me from my baseball and basketball practice in the other house and delayed my weekly trip to the Five and Ten with my mother. Often when she was there, I'd perform a swinging exercise to stir up some breeze around me, using the edges of our kitchen table and washtub as parallel bars. My mother would tell me to stop before I fell and hurt myself, while our visitor commented that "*Santo Gaetano* is full of pepper today. I hope it doesn't rain."

I told Vinnie that after one such remark, I reacted with uncharacteristic rudeness and went next door to shoot baskets. By the time I returned to our side of the hall, Old Stink Pants had just reached the point in *Un Ballo In Maschera* where the sorceress Ulrica summons the King of the Abyss by reminding him that "the owl has hooted three times, the salamander has jumped through fire three times, and the dead have groaned in their tombs three times." I groaned a little myself, recognizing the beginning of the second act. Three more acts to go. Within ten minutes, the King of the Abyss scored another triumph and I returned to the other house.

I wrote to Vinnie, too, about the proliferating animal life in the other house. The cockroaches were particularly bad in the kitchen. During her spare time, my grandmother kept putting smelly paste on pieces of potato which she hid in corners. She also squirted liquids, broadcast deadly seeds across the floors, and knocked fat roaches dead off the walls with swats of her mighty palm. The climate on our side of the hall must have been inhospitable to the insects, but despite my grandmother's valiant efforts, they ran rampant in the other house.

My grandmother was a born killer. I told my brother how a six-inch black creature, all legs and wings, had flown in through a front-room window. My mother and I had beaten a hasty retreat to our house, leaving my grandmother to repulse the terrifying invader with her broom. After sounding the all clear, she had shown us its shriveled corpse. My mother and I cringed.

"Bah, you both have chronic diarrhea," my grandmother said.

Mice, too, had grown bold enough to scurry across the floor in daylight. My grandmother kicked and lunged, but rodents were too fast for her. It was as though the war had unleashed the wrath of the animal kingdom on us. Eventually, she got a cat to take care of the mice. But she could do nothing about the cockroaches.

The war had another unforeseen effect, I told my brother. It seemed to have fired my grandfather with new ambition. He had gone into business for himself.

He left the other house every morning about 6:30 to go to Park Avenue to sell garlic. To us, Park Avenue was not a street of elegant residences, but the boundary line which separated our neighborhood from Black Harlem. Early arrivals in the Puerto Rican immigration were settling around there, and the Avenue was lined with pushcarts and peddlers, both outdoors and inside green, block-long buildings recently built for them at the direction of Mayor LaGuardia. My grandfather stationed himself by the entrance to one of these buildings with a wicker basket full of garlic. I described to Vinnie how, in the evenings, the old man let me help him sort the garlic according to size and arrange it in his basket.

"I cannot write my name," he used to say, "but I can do sums and I can speak Spanish. This head of garlic here is *la ciquita*. That means 'small' in our language."

Playfully, he'd say it over and over again. "*La ciquita. La ciquita.*"

I did not write to Vinnie about the day my grandfather returned from Park Avenue only an hour after he'd left the other house. He had no basket, no money, and his face was covered with blood. He would not answer our questions but, after gingerly washing his face, went to his cot where he stayed for twenty-four hours. When he finally got up, it was clear that he had retired as a small businessman.

Nor did I write anything of what happened a couple of

months later. My mother's agitation was clearly visible when she came to pick me up that noon at P.S. 85, though she assured me everything was all right. But when she served me lunch in *our* house, I knew something was wrong.

"Is it my grandfather?" I asked.

My mother nodded. "He doesn't feel well."

"What's the matter?"

"He's very sick."

She took me back to school, and not until after she'd taken me home to our house again at three o'clock did she tell me my grandfather had died.

"But it's all right," she said. "Don't worry. You won't have to come to the funeral home. The whole family is coming tonight. Your father too. There will be someone to stay with you. Barbara, perhaps. You can play with Tommaso Kennu."

"I can't come to the funeral home?"

"Why upset yourself? Besides, you must write to your brother. Write him from me, as usual. And do not mention anything about your grandfather. We mustn't worry him."

So again that evening and in the evenings that followed, I wrote to my brother, sending him hugs and kisses from his grandfather.

THE FURLOUGH

He had put on forty pounds by the time he came home on his first furlough, in the middle of September. I hardly knew the olive drab giant who sat at the kitchen table in the other house, shaking his head and saying in Sicilian, "But why didn't you write to me that he died? They would have given me an emergency furlough. I should have been here."

"See?" my father said, raising his shoulder. He had taken the week off. "I told you to let him know."

I didn't sleep very well that night in our house with my big brother, bigger than ever, lying next to me. For months, I'd had our bed to myself, free to shift position, spread out, curl up, talk to myself, until sleep arrived. Now I was lying rigid and contracted, feeling the need to blow my nose in the handkerchief under my pillow, but afraid to. I listened to the sound of Vinnie's breathing, waiting for the moment it would become deeper and slower, when I could relax. I concentrated on the happy thought that the next morning was Saturday.

I arose early, sliding myself gingerly out from under

110

Vinnie's massive elbow on my stomach. I was anxious for him to wake up, but he slept on while I washed, he slept on while I had my usual breakfast of coffee mixed with the yolk of an egg, he slept on and on, with his big mouth open, snoring, while I tiptoed in every few minutes to look at him. Finally, he blinked.

"Hello," he said.

"Did you sleep good?"

"Yeah. I was tired. What time is it?"

"About eleven-thirty."

"Where's everybody?"

"In the other house, except Pina, and Pop's out for a walk."

"Oh."

"Today . . ."

"What?"

"Today, I want to play baseball with you." The sentence sounded silly the way it came out. I had stressed every syllable, like the Pledge of Allegiance.

"With the dice?" Vinnie yawned.

"With the bat. Two bats."

"You mean in the other house?"

"Yes."

"We'll see."

"I'm pretty good now, you know. I wrote to you. I bet I can beat the lousy Yankees today."

"Yeah?" He yawned again.

We played after Vinnie had had his breakfast. Until then, I had been the biggest breakfast eater in either house, by virtue of the egg I got in my morning coffee.

When the new, huge Vinnie was confronted by the normal Sicilian breakfast of a cup of black coffee, he informed us: "In the Army I'm used to eating in the morning. You got any eggs?"

He fried himself three of them, was disappointed because there was no bacon, sausage, ham, or cereal around, and finally asked exasperatedly for orange juice.

My mother was horrified. "The juice of an orange? Are you sick? Have another cup of coffee. Or do you want your soup now?"

"Let's go, Vinnie, you ready?" I asked impatiently.

Still yawning, he said he was.

"I got three new baseballs all set," I said. "They're made of one hundred per cent typewriter paper. I been using newspaper myself. You know, I wrote you."

"Oh. Who's up first?"

"I'm always up first. I'm the visiting Dodgers." How could he have forgotten?

"All right, let's start," he said. He could have been talking to a dentist.

"Wait a minute," I said, and cupped my hands around my mouth. "Attention, please, ladies and gentlemen. The batteries for today's game. For the Brooklyn Dodgers, Higbe and Owen. For the New York Yankees—who's pitching for your side, Vin?"

"I dunno. Spud Chandler."

"For the New York Yankees, Chandler and Dickey. Play ball!"

Vinnie's first pitch was a soft, arching blooper which I smacked back off his forehead.

"Hey, take it easy, will you, Tommy?"

"Single," I said.

The next pitch was similar to the first. It had nothing on it. Boom! A double, through the bedroom window into my grandfather's old room where it rattled around under the folded-up cot.

"Pretty good, hah, Vinnie? Men on second and third."

I sent them home on the next pitch with a humming single past Vinnie's right ear.

"Ho, boy. The Yankees is dead," I gloated. "C'mon, pitcher!"

He came on with another cripple pitch. Crack! A home run.

"Almost a triple," I yelled. "Almost went on the fire escape!"

It took my brother Spud Chandler fifteen minutes to put out the side, and he gave up over a dozen runs to the Dodgers in the process.

Kirby Higbe blazed his fast one by the Yankee leadoff man, who didn't even lift the bat from his shoulder.

"Whatza madder, can't you see the ball?"

Vinnie yawned again.

"You still sleepy?"

"Still hungry," he said, one-handedly and half-heartedly swinging at my next pitch and missing it.

I mixed up my stuff beautifully. Fast balls, change-ups, curve balls. I even threw a knuckle ball. Vinnie swung too late or too soon, always too weakly. It was three up and three down quickly.

"Vinnie, you want to go to the Yankee Stadium today?" It was my father, back from his walk.

"No thanks, I have a date," my brother answered.

"A date? With who? With Pina?" my father asked. "Where is she anyway?"

"You know her," my mother said, tightening her lips.

I wished my parents would get off the field.

"No, not with Pina," Vinnie said. "With a buddy of mine and a couple of girls. Game's over, Tommy. You win."

"I win? But it's not an official game yet. We ain't played four and a half innings."

"You win anyway."

"You boys play baseball in the house? Shouldn't do that," my father said. He had never seen one of our games.

"I got to get cleaned up," Vinnie said.

"Aren't you staying for the soup?" my mother asked.

"No. I have a date."

"Let him go," my father said, "he's a man."

"Come on, let's finish the game. At least four and a half innings, so it's official that I win," I said.

"Don't have time, Tommy. You would have beat me anyway. You got such a big lead, I'd never catch up. So I'm forfeiting the game to you. You win nine to nothing."

"Aw, that's no good."

"Sure it is. A forfeit counts just as much in the record book."

I kicked both bats across the front-room floor.

"You ever been to a real ball game?" my father asked me.

"No."

"You want to go to the Yankee Stadium with me?"

"No, it's too hot," my mother answered for me.

"We won't sit in the bleachers. We'll get grandstand seats," my father told her.

"Okay," I said, embarrassed.

"Don't get too much sun," my mother warned. "Be careful. Don't let him get too much sun."

My father's right shoulder rose.

I remember thinking, as my father and I sat quietly watching the real baseball game, that Yankee Stadium was nothing like the other house. I remember very little else, except that the Yankees won.

Vinnie returned late at night, and went out again Sunday morning, saying he'd be back for supper. He wasn't. After eating, my mother and I retired to the front room. She pulled one of the wooden chairs over to the window. I sat in a corner near the bedroom, reading *Action Comics*. Soon my father joined us and began to pace up and down. It was the second time in two days he'd been in the front room of the other house. I didn't remember even one other such occasion. His presence made me more nervous than usual. Every few minutes I retreated to the kitchen, where my grandmother was sewing on her cutaways, to get a glass of water or go to the *beckowzu*. On my fifth trip, she looked at me over her glasses and told me I was behaving like a Neapolitan with St. Vitus's dance.

I could have gone across the hall, or on the fire escape. But my father had been on our side of the hall most of the day, while I stayed in the other house. If I absented myself now, he would surely know I was avoiding him. It was easy on his days off, but this time he had a whole week off.

Besides, it didn't seem right to avoid him too obviously, after he'd taken me to Yankee Stadium that way. So I walked back into the front room, sat down again, and tried to concentrate on the adventures of Superman.

"You all right?" my father asked.

I smiled and nodded.

"You like the game yesterday? Good game, ha?" He spoke in that curious New Orleans-out-of-Camporeale English of his.

I nodded again, and suddenly my father shouted, "Why don't you talk to me? Why the hell don't you talk to your father?"

I was frightened. He had never raised his voice to me before. I started to sweat. What should I say? What did he want to hear? My mother, jolted from her window-gazing by the shout, came to my rescue.

"*Chi c'e?*" she said to my father. "What is it?"

"I asked him why he can't talk to his father," he answered quietly in Sicilian.

If I don't know the answer to his question, I thought, how could she?

"What do you mean?" my mother said. "He talks to you when you ask him something. He always answers."

"It's not enough to answer questions. He should say something out of his own head once in a while, just because he feels like it. How he's doing in school, and what he's learning there, or how he feels. When he feels sick he should tell me."

116

"Thank God he is not sick now. He is sick often enough. Is that what you want, that he should be sick?"

"What I want," my father said, "is that when my son goes to have his heart examined, I should know about it first. Not that you should tell me two years later."

"Thank God he was all right," my mother advised him. "As for telling you what he is learning in school, the new term has just started. There is nothing to tell yet."

My father ignored her explanation. "There's the other one," he said. "He doesn't talk to me either. Why did I bother taking the week off? I've hardly seen him. All right, he's grown up, he has his own life to lead. But why shouldn't he talk to me? Why shouldn't the little one talk to me? The big one didn't want to go to the baseball game yesterday, so I took Tommy. He didn't say a word the whole time. Not a word going to the game, and not a word coming back. We rode on the subway like two deaf mutes."

"Why didn't you say something to him?" my mother asked my father.

"Look," he said, raising his shoulder, "I think you're the one who's to blame for all of this. You've turned my sons against me. What have you told them about me?"

"I? What should I tell them about you? You're their father. I tell them to honor and respect their father. What more can I tell them?"

"You can tell them their father loves them."

"You are the one who must tell them that."

"When I talk to them, they look at the floor, blush, sweat, clear their throats, and leave the room as fast as they can. Why should that be? Do they think I'm going to hit them?"

"They are shy," my mother explained. "Both of them are very shy."

"They're too shy. They're so shy, they're stupid."

"Vincenzo has been away for months. He hasn't seen you. He feels strange. He has hardly talked to me either."

"He was the same way before he ever went in the Army. He was that way when he went to high school. He's been the same since kindergarten, that one. But the little one . . . in Newark, the little one used to laugh and joke with me. We used to play together. What happened to him?"

"He sees you but one day a week," my mother reminded him.

"And he does his best to stay out of sight the whole day."

"Well . . ." my mother said, spreading her hands.

My father sat down across the room from me and said nothing more. While the silence lasted, I never looked up from the comic book. I scarcely moved, turning the pages as quietly as possible. When I got to the end, I started again at the beginning.

"What was it they did to your heart?" my father said at last, in English.

"An electrocardiogram, they call it," I said.

"What is that?"

"They attach like wires to you. First they rub a cream on that burns."

"What was wrong with your heart? Did it bother you?"

"Sometimes at night," I said. "It felt like it was burning."

"Imagination," my father said. "It was probably just your imagination."

"I guess so."

"Your teeth okay now?"

"Oh, I get toothaches once in a while. I got used to my glasses all right, though."

"Good. I'm getting used to mine, too. Now I'm going to have to get false teeth. Mr. Kreiner is recommending a dentist for me. You know, in Newark. Mr. Kreiner's my boss."

"I know."

"How did you do in school last term?"

"Pretty good. I'm going to a new school next year. Junior high."

"Already? You must be pretty smart, ha?"

"I guess so." I blushed. "You know, a long time ago they gave a test to see how smart we were at school and I scored a hundred and sixty-five."

"Wow! I thought the highest mark was a hundred."

"No, this is different."

"Boy."

There was silence again. My mother got up from her place at the window to go into the kitchen to help my grandmother with the cutaways. "Whenever you want to go to bed . . ." she said to me as she passed.

"He'll go to bed in a little while," my father said. "First we'll do a little more talking." But when we were alone in the front room he said nothing for quite a while, even though I'd put the comic book down.

"See, all the good players are in the Army," he said, finally. "DiMaggio, Keller, Henrich, that's the regular outfield."

"I know," I said.

"Those players we saw yesterday can't shine their shoes. Crosetti, Red Rolfe, Joe Gordon, that's the regular infield, you know. I tell you though, the Yanks ain't had a real good first baseman since Lou Gehrig."

"No, that's right," I said.

"The Iron Horse, they called him."

"Yeah, the Iron Horse."

"Buddy Hassett isn't so bad, though."

"No."

A few minutes later he got up from his chair and walked into the kitchen. "I'm going back to work tomorrow," I heard him say in Sicilian.

Vinnie had two days of his furlough left. Maybe there would still be time for us to have some fun together.

THE SAVAGES

Luigi Galvani (1737–1798), an Italian physiologist from Bologna, did research on the ears and genito-urinary tracts of birds before discovering that when a frog's legs make contact with electricity, they twitch. This displeased his compatriot, Volta, for whom the volt was named, but eventually Galvani was vindicated by having many more things named after *him*, including the galvanometer, galvanized iron, and a junior high school in East Harlem.

Galvani JHS, better known as P.S. 83, was located on 109th Street near Second Avenue, and had a bad reputation when I came to it in 1943. It was a decrepit building with, it was said, a lot of tough boys inside. P.S. 85 had been run-down, too. As a matter of fact, its doors closed forever after I finished the sixth grade there. But my classmates, though they were, on the whole, a sturdy bunch, seemed terrified at having to transfer to 83. Mostly of Italian stock, they had heard that Negroes and Puerto Ricans who went to 83 used knives on Italian kids. Not all my classmates at 85 were going to Galvani. Depending on where they lived, some were bound, amid orgies of self-congratulation, for P.S. 172, Otis Junior High School. Despite its American name, Otis was more "Italian" than Galvani. I didn't know the geography on which our transfer depended, but it seemed unfair to my mother, since 172 was closer to where we lived. My mother, who knew nothing of what 83 was supposed to be like, wondered at the prospect of having to walk at least sixty-four blocks a day to get me to and from school, but she said she'd just have to get used to it. She wouldn't hear of my going alone, of course.

My first day at Galvani was even worse than I'd been led to expect. It began in a place called the "home room," where our teacher, Miss Feinsod, welcomed us and explained that, as young adults, we could sit where we liked. I sat at the back. We were, she said, about to be introduced to the departmental system of education. Different teachers taught different subjects. The class of 7A-1 was to meet in the home room with her four times a day—morning, before and after lunch, and again ten minutes before the "last bell" which rang at three-fifteen. At certain times during the week, we would have "home room periods" of forty minutes. During these periods we could study or do homework or, if a majority of the class so voted, hold "discussions." Today being our first day, we would have two such home room periods, now and at the end of the day "for purposes of orientation." She proceeded to call the roll.

There seemed to be a good many more Puerto Ricans than Negroes in my class. Names like Raoul Pujol, Enrique Rodriquez, Jesus Acevedo, and Roberto Martinez sounded strange, but none of their owners seemed particularly ferocious. The oddest name of all belonged to neither a Puerto Rican nor a Negro, but to a thin blond kid sitting across the aisle from me. He was about my size, but looked much tougher. His mouth was compressed, his eyes beady, and he answered to the name of Zircon Roon. He answered to it amid titters from the rest of the class.

Miss Feinsod ignored our amusement and said, "My, what an unusual name. What kind of name is it?"

"What do you mean, what kind of name is it?" he shot back.

"I mean what nationality? Is it Italian, for example?"

"Eye-talian? You kidding?" he sneered.

"I merely meant, Zircon, that some of us in this class are Italian-Americans, others of us are Latin-Americans, and so on," Miss Feinsod said, as though Roon had not been rude at all. "I was asking for the derivation, or rather the extraction . . ."

"Hey, teach, what does that make me?" a large Negro boy interrupted.

"Yeah, yeah." He was abetted by a small chorus from the four or five other Negroes in the class.

"That makes you a black bastid," said the boy who had answered to the name of Raoul Pujol. He probably said it more loudly than he had intended, loud enough for many of the boys around him to laugh uproariously. Loud enough, too, for the Negro questioner to hear, and jump from his seat. "Spick motha-fucka, come 'eah and I beat yo ass."

"After school, black bastid," Raoul Pujol answered. He was immediately seconded by his friends.

To my amazement, Miss Feinsod pretended not to notice anything. After the Negroes and Puerto Ricans had resumed their seats, she went right back to Zircon Roon.

"What I meant to ask, Zircon," she said, "was what nationality are your parents?"

"They're from South Carolina," Roon said, occasioning more laughter and a few boos. Then, to applause and exaggerated cheering, he added, "I'm an American." It seemed to satisfy Miss Feinsod, and she completed calling the roll.

"Oh, class," she added when she'd finished, "I'd nearly forgotten to tell you. We will have a double period each week, eighty minutes in duration, devoted to physical education. Since the facilities for this kind of activity are limited here, this class will be held at The Boys' Club of New York on 111th Street. There you will have the opportunity to play basketball, boxball, exercise . . ."

"Swimming, too, teach?" someone called out of the tumult of delight that accompanied Miss Feinsod's announcement.

"Yes, there is a swimming pool, too."

"Hurray!" Interracial strife was forgotten and I was panic-stricken. The worst I'd had to contend with at P.S. 85 had been the yearly medical examination. Now I had to face unknown perils once a week. The rest of the week didn't look pleasant, either. My combative classmates had so far ignored me, but I had no doubt that before we ever got to the athletic arena, they would discover my inadequacies and notice that I was the only boy in class who still wore knickers. Nor could I expect support from my fellow alumni of P.S. 85. I'd never been exactly popular with them. They'd probably gang up on me with the rest.

I did not have a chance to worry at length. Miss Feinsod handed out our schedules and I was off to a class in Social Studies. Just a few feet from my home room, I heard wild laughter behind me, and shouts of "He got it on 'im, he got it on 'im." Simultaneously, I was knocked off balance by a crushing blow to the base of my spine, and sent hurtling down the hall. I fell, spread-eagled, to the floor, my glasses unhinged from my right ear. Three Negro boys, all of whom seemed bigger than my brother, ran by me, still laughing. One stamped his foot hard next to my ear. Some boys from my home room saw me but none came to my aid. When I adjusted my glasses, I could see an adult male at the end of the hall, peering from the door of a classroom. I got up painfully, retrieved my schedule, and brushed myself off unobtrusively. Moving my hand to the aching spot in my back, I felt a piece of paper wedged into the top of my knickers between two buttons. I cupped it in my hand and extracted it carefully. "KICK MY NIKERS HARD!!" it said. It hadn't taken them long to notice.

I hobbled along, as nonchalantly as possible, checking room numbers against my schedule. Two doors away, I realized that my destination was the doorway in which the man was standing. I entered and sat quickly, hoping not too many of the boys already in the room had witnessed my embarrassment in the hall. About half seemed to be from 7A-1. Zircon Roon was there, a couple of aisles away.

Another bell rang, and the man came inside, pulling the door shut behind him.

"Good morning, boys," he said. "This is Social Studies One and my name is Mr. Fortunato. In Italian it means 'good luck,' which is what I wish each and every one of you."

By noon, I'd also met Mr. Abramowitz, who taught English, and I could walk normally again. My mother, looking considerably agitated, was waiting for me by the school steps, standing beside a fat woman younger than herself. When I reached them, my mother took my hand, but I disengaged it gently because my classmates might see.

"Did you see my son, Johnny?" the fat woman asked me in English. "I'm Johnny Corvolongo's mother. Is he in your class?"

"I don't know," I said. I couldn't remember whether Miss Feinsod had called that name or not.

"It'd be nice if he was in your class. Two Italian boys together. I was just telling your mother what kind of a place this is. Last year one of the spicks stabbed a teacher. As long as they stab each other, who the hell cares. Good riddance, like they say. But to stab a teacher, or, God forbid, an Italian boy? No sir! I ain't gonna let my son stay in this school. I didn't even wanna send him. I made an application with the Sisters, but they says they ain't got room now. You know what I says to them? I says, 'It's all right to take our money,' I says, 'but God forbid when some poor woman like me asks you for a favor,' I says. I says, 'What I'm gonna do? Send my son to school with spicks and boogies and strangers?' So the Sister says if I don't like it I should move. Imagine that? What she says to me? She got no right to say nothing like that to me. I says that to her, I says, 'You got no right to say nothing like that.' So she says back, 'Sorry, absolutely no room now. Maybe next term.' No sir! I ain't letting my Johnny stay here. I'm putting him in Cat'lic school. You know your mother didn't know nothing about what a bad reputation this place got? How come you didn't tell her? Maybe you coulda gone to Cat'lic school. What happened inside this morning?"

"*Beh, signo*," my mother said, approximating the Neapolitan dialect I guessed the fat woman had used with her, "we have to go. It's a long way." She asked me what time I had to be back. As I answered, a tall, very fat boy whom I recognized from the home room came running up.

"Oh, Johnny," Mrs. Corvolongo kissed him. "What happened, honey?"

"A lot of spicks and boogies. Some a them are gonna have a fight, tree o'clock. But there's a few Italians," he said.

"Oh, yeah? That's good. You know this kid here? What's your name? He in your class?"

Johnny looked at me and nodded.

"That's good, that's good," his mother said. "Stick together, boys. We'll be out here waiting at tree o'clock again, but stick together inside, God forbid anything should happen. You know," she turned to me, "I'm sorry I don't remember your name. Anyways, your mother tells me she been coming to leave and get you all the time you been going to school. Me, this is the first time I'm coming for Johnny, and only because it's this lousy place. In grammar school he always come and went by himself. Even here he goes by himself. I just come to take him home, make sure there's no fights from inside. But your mother, she's some careful woman. No good to be too careful, though." She looked at my knickers disapprovingly.

"*Beh, signo, arrivederci*," my mother said impatiently.

"Okay, *signo, arrivederci* tree o'clock. Let's go, honey."

"Was it bad?" my mother asked, on our way home. "What happened?"

"Nothing. They have men teachers."

"To keep the savages in line, sure. Damn this country, that they should make me take you to such a school."

"It's not so bad," I said. "Don't worry."

But the afternoon was worse. Back in our home room, after I'd met yet another teacher, Miss Brine, who taught "Art," Miss Feinsod, worried, perhaps, at the prospect of an after-school rumble the first day, took official notice of the events of the morning.

"America has been called a vast melting pot," she began. "Can anyone tell me what is meant by that phrase?"

No hands were raised, but Miss Feinsod pressed on.

"You must have noticed today, as you went from class to class . . . I trust, by the way, that your first day at the Galvani Junior High School proved enjoyable . . . you must have noticed how many nationalities, how many different kinds of people, how many, as we say, ethnic origins are represented among your fellow students, and among the teachers, too. Some of us are Negroes, others of us have a Latin-American heritage, or an Italian one, there is a sprinkling of several other backgrounds, and yet we are all of us Americans. This very school was named for an Italian, and I, myself, am from a Russian background."

She was interrupted by a voice from the middle of the room. "Hey, teach, I thought you was a Jew."

"Yes, I am of the Jewish faith. My religion, that is to say, is Judaism. But my parents were born and brought up in Russia. Many people are confused about the Jewish faith, and I am happy to have this opportunity of clearing up this problem. Even some Jews consider Judaism a nationality, or a race, or some unique kind of ethnic grouping, and not solely a religion. I do not share their view. To me, Judaism is a religion just as Roman Catholicism, which many of you profess, is a religion, or as Protestantism is a religion. Well, Protestantism is not really a religion, but a group of religions. Or, one might call it a religion composed of many different sects. I trust I am making myself clear."

There was a laugh from the back row right behind me. I heard someone whisper, "You making yourself clear all right. Spread your legs some more."

I looked up from my folded hands to watch Miss Feinsod. She was seated on the front edge of her desk, smiling and continuing to talk in a confidential tone. Her knees were a few inches apart and her dress had moved up to show part of the dark tops of her stockings. I sensed that not just the boy who had whispered behind me, but most of the class was alert to Miss Feinsod's hemline.

Apart from her stocking tops, Miss Feinsod was really not much to look at. I'd guess she was close to fifty. She wore her dull hair mannishly, her face was entirely too pink, and thick glasses made her eyes almost invisible. Her lips were nearly as thick as those of my Negro classmates, and her nose was even broader than theirs.

"We had an unfortunate incident here this morning," she went on, "in which racial epithets were used, carelessly and unthinkingly. It was not only unfortunate but stupid, since every one of us in this country is as good as every one else."

"How good are you in bed, baby," the whisperer behind me wondered.

"Not everything in this country is perfect, of course. There are slums, for instance, where people live in overcrowded, squalid conditions. But this is all the more reason why we must all work together, side by side, hand in hand, to overcome these conditions, instead of fighting among ourselves."

Zircon Roon raised his hand.

"Yes, Zircon?"

"Is this a slum, Miss Feinsart?" he asked through his tough, tight lips.

"My name is Miss Feinsod, Zircon," she said, looking through a window at 109th Street, "and this neighborhood, well, I'd call it a *semi*-slum. I mean, it's *almost* a slum. I think it's *becoming* a slum. This is a most interesting neighborhood, you know. Jews lived here when they first came to America, and then Irish, then Italians, and now our Negro and Puerto Rican Americans are moving in. It isn't the people who are making it a slum, however, but society." She was growing excited, bobbing up and down on the desk, showing more leg.

"No, this country is far from perfect, but we are a

democracy. In a democracy, you can change things. We are now in a great war against totalitarianism, a great war which will test if our own system is to survive. If it is to survive, we'll have to make it better. We will have to tear down the slums and build decent places for people to live." Her garter snaps were showing.

Behind me, excitement raged around the whisperer. I sneaked a look at him. He was a pimply-faced Puerto Rican who seemed older than the two boys on either side of him. All three were leering and whispering at each other now, not even looking at Miss Feinsod any more. I didn't understand what they were saying.

". . . you got a scum bag . . ."

". . . sure, man, jerking off right here . . ."

". . . you thinking about?"

". . . I always got to pee afterwards."

The pimply-faced boy moved his hands mysteriously under his desk.

". . . jerk off . . ."

". . . jerking off . . ."

"Martinez is jerking off."

They laughed loudly enough for Miss Feinsod to hear, but she paid no attention.

"George Washington Carver was born a slave. Yet he rose to be a great American, a great benefactor to mankind." So saying, she slid forward off the front of her desk, while her dress pulled up over the bottom of her long girdle. There was a pleased gasp from part of the class, while Miss Feinsod retreated behind her desk.

Behind me, the whispering reached a crescendo.

"He's coming."

"He already come, man, see."

"There it is, boys, nice scum."

". . . scum . . ."

". . . nice, juicy scum."

I turned to peek at them again. Martinez had lifted a thin, rubbery, semi-transparent bag onto his desk, while his friends, and I, stared in fascination. He saw me looking.

"What you want, football head?" he asked. "You want to drink some of the juice in this bag, man?" He held the object toward my face.

His friends laughed. "Hey, cherry pit, you want some scum?"

As I turned away, I felt the thing plop onto my head. I grabbed at it quickly and shoved it into my desk drawer. My hand came away wet and sticky. The laughter grew more widespread.

"Quiet, boys," Miss Feinsod cautioned. "What's going on?" She saw that I was the red-faced center of attention. "You, there, what's your name again?"

"Thomas Martana."

"Well, what is it, Thomas?"

"Nothing."

"Have you been paying attention?"

"Yes."

"What have I been talking about then?" She moved in front of her desk again. There was nothing attractive about her at all.

"You were talking about how America is the land of opportunity," I said.

"Good. That's right. Now, come to order."

When the home room period ended, I rose hurriedly, touching my head, feeling for any of that strange fluid that might have dribbled onto it. I bumped straight into Zircon Roon, who pushed me forcefully against a desk.

"Watch where you're going, dope," he said.

"Boys, boys," Miss Feinsod said. "Go home, the bell rang."

I walked cautiously out the door. In the hall, Martinez and his friends had been joined by Raoul Pujol, the boy who had proposed settling his differences with Negroes after school, and several others. None of the Negroes were anywhere in sight. Miss Feinsod seemed to have averted a race riot, though not in the way she'd intended. Martinez held the little bag, which he'd apparently retrieved from my desk.

"Hey, football head, here's some nice, juicy scum," he said, tossing it at me. It bounced off my glasses and to the floor. Laughter and cries of "football head" and "cherry pit" followed me all the way out to my mother. Puerto Ricans gave nicknames just like Sicilians, I thought, wondering at the symbolism of "cherry pit."

Tuesday went by without incident. Martinez and his friends were almost nice to me when they saw me in the morning. "Hey, cherry pit, how's the knickers?" But Wednesday was to be Boys' Club day, and I began worrying about it as soon as my mother and I were home Tuesday afternoon.

"Tomorrow we are going to a place called *lu boisi clubbu*," I announced. "It's where we're supposed to play ball and do exercises and swim."

"Mother of God! Swim! Don't you dare go in the water. The ancients said, *Fire and water, give them room.* A fine thing to learn in school, to drown."

"I know," I said. "I don't want to go."

"Tell them I forbid it."

"They won't excuse me just for that."

"No? A mother has no say in this country? You're right. In this country they want everything written down and spelled out. Very well. Write a note and I'll sign it. Say you're a delicate child and can't swim or exert yourself."

On a sheet of my typewriter paper, I wrote in ink: "Gentlemen, My son Thomas Martana is too weak to play ball or go swimming. I would appreciate it if you excused him from these activities. Very truly yours, . . ."

"Sign here," I said. "But it probably won't do any good. They'll want a note from a doctor."

Our athletic instructor, over six feet tall, had a bullet-shaped head of bristly hair. He wore a T-shirt emblazoned with the insignia of The Boys' Club of New York, over which was draped a whistle on a string.

"Okay, guys," he barked, as soon as our class filed onto the gym floor. "Let's get a few things straight. There's gonna be no fighting and no wise behavior around here. You're here to enjoy yourself like you're supposed to. You play fair with me, and I'll play fair with you. Get wise with me, and I turn mean. Starting next week everybody shows up here in gym clothes, that's shorts and a T-shirt. Those guys that wear glasses have to take them off, or get a guard. When we start swimming later on, you won't need a bathing suit. There's no girls here."

He paused for laughter before continuing. "Since you don't have the proper clothes yet, we won't go through any formal exercises today. Next week, remember, shorts and T-shirt, and a combination lock. Everybody will be assigned a locker. Okay now, let's play a little boxball."

I approached amid bouncing rubber balls and handed him the note. "Look, kid, this is ridiculous," he said, giving it right back to me. "You look okay to me. You want to be excused, you bring a note from your doctor. Now get in there and play."

He blew his whistle. "Wait a minute, Martana, wait a minute. Take your glasses off first."

When I told him I couldn't see without them, he allowed me to keep them on, warning me to be careful. Then he blew his whistle again.

"Fellas, be sure to include this guy in the game. I hear he's a ringer. A regular Joe DiMag. There he is, Kid Knickers."

Martinez accepted me on his team grudgingly. "You really know how to play, football head?" he asked.

"Sure," I said.

"Okay, you're leadoff man and we're up first. Get up to the plate and wait for a good one, man. You only get one swing."

As I stood at the plate, I tried to conceal my nervousness by swinging my right arm loosely. From the front-room windows, I'd seen boxball played on 117th Street.

The game was like baseball, except that you had to hit the ball, a rubber "spaldeen," with your hand.

"Hey, close your hand, cherry pit," I was advised by one of my teammates. "Hit the ball with your fist."

"Sure you don't want to take off your glasses?" asked the whistle-blower, standing off the first base line.

I shook my head. Zircon Roon was pitching for the opposition. I noticed that most of his teammates were Italian kids from P.S. 85. All of mine seemed to be Puerto Ricans. Roon's first pitch hit the floor two feet in front of me and bounced crazily past my fist.

"Hook, hook, he's trowin' a hook," Martinez hollered. "Teach, he's trowin' a hook. Ain't that against the rules?"

"Come on, play ball," the whistle-blower said. Roon glared and threw four more pitches before I swung and missed. I stepped to the sidelines, too far, into somebody else's boxball game.

"Hey, get off the field, knickers."

"Get off the field, muh-fucka."

The whistle-blower grabbed me and spun me out of the way. "You can't hit a homer every time, DiMag, so don't go trying to jump the team."

I tried to make believe I was in the front room of the other house. I thought of all the mighty blasts I'd hit, including the triple that had sailed onto the fire escape. It was no use. This was different. I struck out three times in the inning.

In the field, they put me at third base. In the first inning nothing was hit to me. But in the second inning, I bobbled two chances. In the third, I succeeded in stopping a ball with my chest, but then couldn't pick it up to throw it to first base.

At bat, in the fifth inning, I finally hit the ball a glancing blow and sent a dribbler toward the pitcher. I was so surprised that I didn't start running until Zircon Roon had retrieved the ball and already thrown it to first base. My teammates cursed me and wanted to bench me, but the whistle-blower, who was still watching, ignoring the other two contests in progress, wouldn't let them. It seemed to me that by the end of that interminable game, I must have made about twenty-five of my team's twenty-seven outs. I knew I could never return to The Boys' Club.

When I told my mother that the note she'd signed had been rejected, she said that, if he were still alive, Dr. Oranzino would probably compose an acceptable one without any fuss.

Dr. Oranzino lived where he had worked, on 116th, a street of doctors, lawyers, and funeral homes. He had been the Martana and Tarantola doctor before we'd moved to Newark, my mother said, and had been old even then. His name plate, still affixed to the outside of the building, encouraged us considerably. We were greeted by a tiny old woman.

"Eh, *signo,*" she said, shaking her head, "my brother is old. He does not practice. But if you wish, I will call him."

She went out, leaving my mother and me to fidget and look at their faded parlor furnishings for several minutes. When she reappeared, she was supporting a man even tinier than herself, wearing a threadbare bathrobe and so bent over that he could not look up at us. She deposited him onto a straight-back chair. He looked as though he might topple forward at any moment, and roll right out of the room.

"Eh, *signora*," he croaked, "my dear sister has told me who you are. I remember you well. And your mother, how is she?"

"*Bene, grazie*," my mother answered.

"And your father?"

"In the sky."

"Oh, too bad, too bad. He was much younger than me. I do not practice any more, but if there is some favor I can do. How old would you say I am, *signora*?"

He seemed unaware that his bathrobe had slipped open as he spoke. His sister came and covered him.

"*Scusa*, please," she said to us, "*scusati*."

"I'm sorry we bothered you, Doctor," my mother said. "There is nothing we want. We just came to visit an old friend, nothing more."

"Very well," the ancient healer replied. "I always admired your family. A good family, the Tarantolas. *Addio, signora. Addio*, sonny."

"He was a good doctor," my mother said on our way home. "He didn't believe in pills. He always gave liquid medications or powders. And he always cured the sickness. He cured me of the terrible headaches I had right after your brother was born. He cured me with a wonderful blue powder. Now he is not even aware when his little shriveled biscuit is showing. That's old age for you. Well, let those brutes at school drown if they want to. Let them sweat till they melt in a pool of rancid water. My son is not going to join them. We don't need a doctor's note. I should buy my son short underwear to expose himself and run himself to death? Savages! You'll just stay home. Let them try and get you. You just won't go to school on Wednesdays any more."

And I didn't, all through the seventh grade.

THE DORMITORY

My grandfather's cot stayed folded for less than a year after he died. Soon after I entered Galvani, Barbara left Uncle Charlie, taking Thomas Kenneth with her to Georgia.

"*Americani, cori di cani* [Americans, hearts of dogs]," my grandmother advised her elder son when he moved back to the other house. "How you ever found such a creature in the first place, I never understood, although the way you and that friend of yours used to go off in those days, I knew you could be up to nothing good. What was his name? Michele? Michele Mangiamele [Michael the honey-eater]. How that car of his had to cough for half an hour before he got it going! It should have died of consumption. What did you expect to find, riding around in the godforsaken wilderness of *La Giorgia*, Queen Margarita? That you should marry the way you did, outside the Church, without even telling your mother till the deed was done! What could you expect but disaster? Barbara! The very name should have warned you."

Uncle Charlie grew impatient at these reminiscences.

"Listen," he hollered in Sicilian, "one thing has got to be understood. As long as I'm here, I don't want her name mentioned in this house."

He glared at my grandmother, my mother, and me, in turn. "Tell my sister, too, when she gets home. Why you people let her run wild, I don't know. You want to warn people, warn her."

My grandmother sighed, and helped Charlie open the cot. " '*Beddu, che beddu lu beddu,*' Carnival Face used to say. *How beautiful is the bed.* That's all he was good for, resting. He was a master rester. Whatever kind of bed he's in now, I hope it's full of bedbugs. If you can see me, Carnival Face, I want you to know that this black dress I'm wearing means nothing. It's so people won't talk. My heart is not black, it is dancing. And don't think I'm going to keep it on for the rest of my life. Hah! Three years at most, Carnival Face."

"Hey," Charlie protested. "What is this about Carnival Face?"

"Your father, the *ricuttaru.*"

"*Brava*, nice, nice. A nice way to talk about my father. As long as I'm in this house, nobody calls my father Carnival Face or a ricotta dealer."

I didn't like the way Charlie was giving orders as soon as he moved in. I was sorry he and Barbara had broken up, primarily because I would miss Thomas Kenneth. Just recently Thomas Kenneth had apologized to me for being three years younger, but pointed out that in the future our age disparity would not seem so great. "In two years I'll be ten and you'll be thirteen, and in four years, when I'm twelve, you'll be fifteen," he'd said, "and when we're real big I'll be seventeen and you'll be twenty. Then we can go out together with girls and have real fun."

I'd agreed it would be nice.

Now he was gone, and his father, who worked as a night watchman, was going to be asleep on the cot all day.

After a few weeks, Charlie was fired from his job. From something my mother told me, I guessed that he must have been caught drunk. She related the incident haltingly and only because I asked her on our way to school one day why she and my grandmother had been whispering and giggling lately every time Charlie got up to go to the *beckowzu*. She had been having her coffee one morning, she said, and my grandmother had been stuffing completed cutaways into a shopping bag, when they'd seen Charlie emerge unsteadily from my grandfather's room, clutching the bedclothes to himself to conceal the undershorts in which he slept. Instead of entering the *beckowzu*, he'd started opening the front door. All the time he was fiddling with the locks, the women told him he was making a mistake, but all they got in response were drunken groans. My mother stopped her story there, but I deduced that Charlie had succeeded in peeing in the hall, because during one of her fits of giggling, I'd heard my grandmother say that "if Filippo saw it, he probably thought it was the cat." My mother had countered that her brother must have thought he was back in the old building on First Avenue, where the *beckowzu* had been in the hall. I was sure from all this that Charlie had acquired a new nickname.

142

Not exactly cheerful when he'd moved back, Charlie grew more morose after losing his job. He still slept all day, and some nights he wouldn't talk at all during dinner. Other nights he spoke of going back to Sicily after the war. He'd last seen it when he was eight or nine years old, but the way he talked, he couldn't wait to return.

"*Si, signore,* after the war I'm going to take a nice long trip to Camporeale, and if I like it, I may never come back."

"You may never get to go," my grandmother told him one night, "for this war may never end."

"What are you talking about?" Charlie said testily. "Italy has already surrendered. It's only a matter of time before the others do."

"Oh, yes?" my grandmother challenged. "Then why are they taking your brother into the Army? Because the war is over?"

She'd heard the news from Aunt Concetta, she said, who'd gone to *Li Roggispiti* to tell her.

"I didn't want to spoil my family's dinner," my grandmother explained, "but God has willed that I tell you now. Concetta said not even Vito Marcantonio can get Nicola out of it. Can you imagine? They are taking fathers of families."

"They're taking Nick?" Charlie sounded incredulous, but amused.

"Isn't that what I just said? This is what The Green Rose has brought us to. But plenty of people are lining their pockets, plenty of people have fat jobs." My grandmother eyed Charlie meaningfully. "Plenty of people are getting rich while others are out of work and others are being taken from their families."

Charlie laughed. "Ha, they're taking Nick. Things must really be in bad shape then. You're right, the war ain't gonna end soon. Or if it does, the United States is gonna be on the losing side. Hee-hee, what a soldier he'll make."

Charlie was laughing the way he used to at my father's stories. He hadn't laughed that way since he'd come back to the other house.

"The buttonhole maker told me her nephew got a war job that pays two hundred and fifty dollars a week," my grandmother said pointedly. "Have you ever made such money, son of mine?"

"Some soldier. A general. A commander-in-chief, ho-ho-hee-hee."

"What are you laughing at?" my mother asked. "Maybe they'll take you soon."

"Me? First place, I'm six years older than the general. Second place, I'm not a general. Not even a private. My brother's the general. Hee-hee, Nicholas, the general."

After dinner, when he shaved as usual before the big mirror between the kitchen windows, he sang a Neapolitan song, *"Ruselle 'e Maggio"* ["Roses of May"]. He put on a clean white shirt and a tie, and carefully arranged the sparse strands of hair across the top of his head.

"Will you be home late?" my grandmother asked.

"I'm just going down to First Avenue for a cup of coffee and to talk over military affairs. Ho-ho-ho."

"The Hallway Pisser is happy," my grandmother observed when he'd left. "It will probably rain tomorrow."

Soon, not only Charlie was in bed all day but Pina as well. Pina slept less soundly than her brother, however.

"She is driving me crazy," my grandmother wailed one morning while she was stuffing cutaways into the shopping bag. "She wakes up and takes a drink from the bottle she keeps under the bed, she falls asleep for five minutes, wakes up to vomit, and takes another drink. It was that evil Carmela who taught her this. The one who claimed to be Sicilian. But I chased that slut away once and for all. And so we discovered America, the America of bad companions and drunken women. I shudder when I must get into bed. Imagine. I lie awake all night praying my daughter will not take too many drinks, will not throw up too many times."

After the other house became an all-day dormitory I could no longer practice baseball or basketball. But then, the skills I had diligently achieved before Vinnie's furlough had left him unimpressed and had deserted me when I'd had to play at The Boys' Club. So it really didn't matter very much.

THE MAFIOSO

My father never commented, but my mother saw Pina's condition and Charlie's return to the other house as visitations of my grandfather's curse condemning his family to the Bowery. At the same time she grew increasingly worried about Vinnie. Often she seemed to be talking to herself inside. She would move her lips without opening her mouth. Aloud, she said her heart was heavy.

"Your brother has stayed in this country so far, but who knows where they are about to send him. I fear a disaster," she explained.

Then the word came that Vinnie had been sent to Hawaii.

"There is no fighting there," I told her. "He's in no danger at all."

"Holy Mother of God, I thank you," she said. "Now please keep him there until the war is over and bring him home safely to me."

Even though her forebodings about Vinnie had proved baseless, her health began to suffer. She walked the sixty-four blocks to and from P.S. 83 with difficulty. She lost

weight. She developed a persistent cough. My grandmother, after consultation with Nick's wife, Concetta,
brought home the name of a doctor.

"He was born here but he went to medical school in
Italy because he wanted to learn the right way," she told us.

"I have no need of doctors," my mother said.

But when almost daily toothaches were added to her
woes, she conceded she had need of a dentist. Wednesday
mornings, not having to take me to school, she went to
Dr. Connovi. Every week she returned with one or two
fewer teeth.

Meanwhile, her cough got no better. Finally, she felt
so badly one day that she kept me home, even though it
wasn't Wednesday. On her way to work that morning, my
grandmother stopped at Concetta's and asked her to have
Dr. Gaione come.

My mother was preparing my lunch in the other house
as I sat at the kitchen table, continually asking her how
she felt and being continually reassured that everything
was all right, when Dr. Gaione arrived. He was a tall man
whose crew cut and bow tie made him appear younger
than he was. He greeted my mother in Neapolitan-
accented Italian and me in East Harlem-accented English.

"You are cooking soup of lentils, *signora?*"

"Yes, for my son."

"Ah, a wonderful smell. It calls to mind the soup my
own mother made. Why aren't you in school today, young
man? Aren't you feeling well either?"

"I couldn't take him," my mother answered.

"So you accompany him to school? Fine, fine. One can't

147

be too careful these days. It is rare one finds such prudence, however. Tell me, where do you go to school, young man?"

I told him, but he got suddenly preoccupied looking into his bag, and did not answer "Fine, fine," until he'd fished out a thermometer and vigorously shaken it down.

The thermometer wobbled unsteadily in my mother's mouth.

"Galvani, eh? So you go to a school named for a famous opera singer."

"Opera singer?"

Dr. Gaione laughed boisterously. "Just a joke. Wanted to see if you'd catch me. You know some people think the only things we do is sing and play baseball."

My mother grunted that the thermometer had been in her mouth long enough.

"What are you studying at Galvani, young man?"

Before I could answer, Uncle Charlie, sleepy-eyed and clutching his blanket, appeared, staggering, in slow motion, to the *beckowzu*. My mother grunted again.

"Another patient?" the doctor asked.

My mother removed the thermometer and handed it to him, and spit into the sink. "Just a sleeper," she said. "My brother works nights."

"There's a little fever," Dr. Gaione said, motioning to her to undo the top buttons of her housedress.

As soon as he'd made it to the *beckowzu*, Charlie pulled the chain, presumably so his urination would not be heard by a stranger.

"I'm studying English, Social Studies, Mathematics, you know, things like that," I said.

148

"That's fine, fine, son." The doctor pressed his stethoscope to my mother's chest.

The noise of flushing subsided, and Charlie's stream came through loud and clear.

"Cough," Dr. Gaione ordered.

When Charlie emerged, Dr. Gaione turned to watch him stumble back to his room.

"Cough again, *signora*," he said.

After he'd examined her, front and back, he told her, "There's some congestion there. We must observe it carefully." Then, switching to English, he said, "Actually, a few days in the hospital are what she needs, but I know these Italian women. Suggesting they go to the hospital is like telling them they're ready for the undertaker. She has what we call rales in her chest. Kind of a rattle. Would you like to listen?"

I declined his offer, listening instead to the sounds in the rooms beyond the kitchen. Before the settling noises from Charlie's cot had subsided, they were augmented by creaks from Pina's bed. In a few seconds, my aunt was in the kitchen in her underwear, holding on to the wall for support.

"Another sleeper?" the doctor inquired.

Pina smiled weakly and said hello.

"*Mia sorella*," my mother explained. "My sister."

The new noises from the *beckowzu* could not be drowned out by flushing.

"Excuse me if I overstep, *signora*, but your sister seems to be throwing up. Is she ill?"

149

My mother shrugged and said there was probably something wrong with her sister's stomach.

"No doubt," Dr. Gaione agreed, sitting down at the table. He started to write a prescription and interrupted himself to peer into his bag again.

"No pills," my mother cautioned him. "I cannot take pills."

"It's not hard, *signora*. I'm just looking for some samples I have here and you can take one right now. You'll see how easy it is. A little water and, poof, down it goes. I know so many women like yourself, *signora*, who say they can't take pills. Well, you'll just have to learn. You want to get well, don't you?"

He looked up from his bag when Pina came out.

"Okay?" he smiled.

"Okay," Pina replied, holding on to the *beckowzu* doorknob.

"You're very young-looking to be your sister's sister."

She started lurching toward her room.

"Wait a second, please. How do you feel now? What was it, something you ate?"

"That's a laugh, something I ate." She'd made it to another doorknob, the one on the front door.

"If you'd like me to examine you . . ."

"Look, mister . . ."

"Excuse me. I'm Dr. Gaione. I was called here on account of your sister."

"What's the matter with her?"

"Some bronchial congestion."

"Oh. I don't have any congestion."

150

"Maybe not. But you're obviously not feeling well. It's not that I'm trying to drum up business. I just thought . . ."

"Stop thinking and let me get back to bed before I fall down," Pina shouted.

There was a loud, angry "Shushh," from Uncle Charlie.

Pina staggered off and Dr. Gaione resumed fishing for his sample pills. When he'd found them, he drew a glass of water at the sink, startling a fat cockroach near the faucet.

My mother gagged, coughed, turned red, and finally swallowed a pill.

"*Signora*, have you a little jar?" the doctor asked.

"I have plenty of jars," my mother assured him.

"Very well. Whenever you cough, I want you to spit into such a jar. Make sure the jar is clean first, of course. Better boil it. When I return Saturday morning, I want to take it with me and look at it. Now have your son take this prescription to your druggist and continue with those pills. That wasn't hard, was it?"

Just a few minutes after he'd left, my mother said she felt better already.

"He guessed the right pill. The only doctor who has ever done that."

I reminded her of Dr. Oranzino. She reminded me that he'd never prescribed pills.

"Pills are dangerous," she said. "I've had to throw away many of them in my lifetime, starting in Camporeale."

"How could you get better if you didn't take your medicine?"

"You are too young to understand these things. Your

godfather, Overflowing Chamberpot, gave me a pill once during the time of my headaches. 'Just an aspirin, *cara cummare*,' he said. First it stuck in my throat and wouldn't go down. When it finally did, I saw a blazing red light and heard a hundred lions roaring. My head weighed thirty tons. It took me a year to get over it. Pills have opium in them, and cocaine. Like those malefactors gave to your father."

"But the pill this doctor gave you was all right?"

"He guessed it. At last someone guessed the right pill for my sickness. Let us thank the Madonna. Tomorrow, I will take you to school."

"Tomorrow is Wednesday," I reminded her.

"The next day, then. If the weather is good, I will take you for a walk tomorrow, to the Five and Ten."

"Are you going to get the prescription filled?"

"Certainly. These are the right pills. Tomorrow, when we go for our walk."

On Saturday, Old Stink Pants had been gone for a couple of hours, my grandmother had returned from her morning's work, and I was alone with the radio in our house, when I heard the vigorous step of Dr. Gaione on the stairs. I waited a few minutes, and went into the other house. The doctor was still apologizing for being so late. He said he'd had one emergency after another. He greeted me, and then complimented my grandmother on her lovely family, "two fine daughters and a son."

"Another son is going in the Army," my grandmother told him, "and I have had, not four, but nine children."

"Aha, the others are all married, I suppose," said the doctor.

"Dead," she corrected.

"I see." He handed my mother the thermometer and, after she'd put it in her mouth, asked her if she'd been taking the pills.

She grunted affirmatively. I knew she hadn't been taking the three a day he had prescribed, but I had seen her take at least one more since Wednesday.

While Dr. Gaione listened to my mother's chest, he seemed to be trying to peek into the rooms beyond the kitchen.

"Fine, much better. Your temperature's down, too," he said. "Oh *signora* Tarantola, sorry about your other five children. And how is your younger daughter?"

My grandmother smoothed her lap. "The children all died young," she said, "two days, two months, ten weeks, six months. One lived for five and a half years. As for my youngest . . . my daughter has associated with evil companions. She will find the right road, however. Her mother will see to that."

Dr. Gaione lowered his voice confidentially. "Pardon me, *signora*, but does she drink to excess?"

"She drinks a little wine," my grandmother answered, still smoothing her lap.

"There is help for such people. If you don't mind, I'd like to talk to her."

My grandmother shrugged. "My children are asleep. My son works nights and my daughter has not been well."

"I don't want to talk to your son, only to your daughter," Dr. Gaione persisted. "No charge."

"How much for me?" my mother asked, a little petulantly.

"Three dollars."

She went to her purse and asked if she should continue spitting into a jar.

"Oh. I'll take the jar with me, *signora*. But do continue. Use another jar. I have no doubt you've improved. Today your chest sounded very much better. But your sister . . ." He looked again at my grandmother. I saw my mother's lips move in quiet agitation.

My grandmother spread her hands. "Very well, Doctor, as you wish," she said.

Later, she was to hail Dr. Gaione as a saviour.

"Suffice it to say that he is Italian. He took my little Pina from that bed and set her on her feet again. It was a miracle, a miracle accomplished by God, a mother's prayers, and a doctor with the soul of a Sicilian, of a *Mafioso*."

THE BLEACHERS

The Christmas Eve party of 1943 was also a farewell party for Nick, a celebration of Charlie's new job, and a reconciliation between the brothers, arranged by my father.

After a lukewarm handshake, Nick and Charlie got along so jovially that I was tense all night, anticipating the kind of calamity the ancients said always followed uncharacteristic behavior. They joked about Nick's departure for the Army, about Charlie's forthcoming career as a waxer of floors, about my brother's non-combat record, and even about Nicholas Tarantola, Jr., whom Charlie met that evening for the first time. Nick congratulated Charlie on having "got rid" of Barbara, Charlie congratulated Nick on the recent birth of little Vittoria Tarantola, and they both congratulated Pina on her victory over Demon Rum. They twitted my father for talking too much, and me for talking too little. I was happy to see my uncles leave, although Charlie only went as far as across the hall, to the other house.

Afterwards, my father reflected that, with Nick in the Army and Charlie working Monday through Friday nights, the regular Monday get-togethers at our house would be no more.

"I think I'm going to take Sundays off from now on," he said. "The three of us could go to the movies after dinner, maybe. Sunday is a better day than Monday."

My mother looked at him quizzically.

"It is the day of rest," my father continued. "Your brother will be off, your mother won't have as many coats to sew, and Tommy won't have to go to school. When the warm weather comes, maybe Tommy will want to go to the ball games with me. We can still go to the movies at night, after the game."

I could tell it was my mother's turn to think about the ancients' predictions of calamity.

But my father made good his promise, and soon she and I were accompanying him on Sunday afternoons to the Cosmo on 116th Street or the RKO on 125th Street. After a while, he widened our horizons still more, and took us to the rococo palaces downtown where they had a movie plus a stage show, and where I imagined Carlo Buti had left his heart. Though my mother understood little of the dialogue, she seemed to enjoy going. She particularly liked period dramas. "The ancient stories are the best, the movies of the long dresses," she would say after we'd seen one. At home, however, she continued to talk to herself in that odd, soundless way of hers. Despite always coming home from them with a headache, I enjoyed going to the movies too. I wrote detailed reviews for my brother.

When the baseball season started, I accepted my father's

invitation to go to the games with him. The first couple of times, we sat in the grandstand, as we had at the first game I'd attended, during Vinnie's furlough the year before. But the third week, on our way to Yankee Stadium, my father told me that when he'd gone to games alone he'd always sat in the bleachers.

"The sun never bothers me," he said. "I guess you don't like the sun."

I told him I didn't mind it.

"They're not regular seats in the bleachers, just benches. I think the benches in the Polo Grounds are a little wider than those in the Stadium, but they have more splinters. You can't have everything."

I smiled and shook my head.

"The trouble is, you can never lean back. You think that will bother you?"

I said I didn't think it would.

"Well, if you want to try it, today is a good day for it. It's so cool, the sun will feel good. In the summer we can go back to the grandstand."

I nodded agreement.

"I think you'll like the bleachers. It's a different type of fan sits there. They appreciate the game more. Although, these days, there isn't that much to appreciate."

"Did you read that the Browns are gonna get a player with one arm?" I asked.

Startled at my volunteering a remark, my father laughed and said, "Yeah. I hear his arm is very strong, though. That should be something to see, a man swinging a bat with one arm. And in the outfield, supposing he's gotta make a fast throw after catching the ball, how the hell is he gonna do it?"

"I guess maybe they'll put him at first base."

"That's right. You're right, that's the best place for him."

I took to the bleachers immediately. The players seemed miles away and sometimes I had to squint and push up my glasses at an angle to see home plate, but I enjoyed the comradeship and knowledgeability of the fans. The same people were there every week, sitting in more or less the same spots. Most of them attended both Yankee Stadium and the Polo Grounds, as we did.

In the Stadium, my father and I sat three aisles away from the right field bull pen, about halfway up between the fence and the scoreboard, near an old Negro man whom neighboring fans referred to as the Preacher. The Preacher was a zealous Yankee fan with some odd superstitions. He believed that if a pitcher started the game by throwing a strike, he'd be knocked out of the box before the day was out. He considered the fourth inning, not the seventh, lucky for the Yankees. And whenever a visiting batter had run the count to two balls and two strikes with two men out, the Preacher became tremendously excited, rising from his seat to shout that the poor man had "the three deuces on him" and was a "dead duck."

The Preacher occasionally doffed his skimmer in appreciation of a Yankee rally, but he never removed his jacket or unbuttoned his vest. He didn't even loosen his tie. All around us, however, sat men who had removed their shirts and undershirts and rolled up their trouser legs. A few took

off their shoes and socks as well. My father never wore a
tie to the games, and usually took off his shirt, but never
his undershirt. He said he was too hairy and didn't want
to shock anybody. For all his hairiness he was nearly totally
bald, and since he always went hatless in summer, his
head was nicely tanned. My own disrobing didn't go beyond undoing the top two buttons of my shirt and rolling
up my sleeves.

Oddly enough, our favorite seat in the Polo Grounds
bleachers—to the left of the clubhouse, about twelve rows
up from the fence—was close to the spot where another
fully clothed fan sat. Fat Leonard, in addition to his shirt,
tie, vest, jacket, and official Giant baseball cap, also wore a
raincoat, even on the hottest, sunniest days. He was further encumbered by a huge pair of field glasses around his
neck and three or four books under his right arm. As far as
I could tell, he never raised the glasses to his eyes or lowered his books to the bench. Occasionally, he shouted ge-
ographical, recondite remarks to the players, for all of
whom he had his own pet names. He might yell, "Watch
out for Sarasota, Butch," for example, or "Peoria or bust,
Highpockets!" The rest of the time he muttered to himself. At the end of the game, he would greet all the Giants
individually as they trotted toward the clubhouse. "Hi,
Bimbo," "What say, Specs?" "Atta way to go, Gable." A
few of the players would look up and wave.

My father and I rarely talked to the other fans or to
each other. In the beginning he used to ask me whether I
wanted peanuts or ice cream or hot dogs, but since I never
did, he stopped asking. On the hottest days, he'd have a

beer, offering me the first sip. I occasionally accepted. Also on hot days, he'd take my handkerchief and his own, wet them at the water fountain under the bleachers, and place them on our heads. He repeated the process every few innings.

As the season went on, whenever there was an exciting play on the field, I'd jump up to cheer or boo, as unrestrained as though my father weren't sitting beside me. Sometimes he'd jump up too. A couple of times we even grabbed one another in the euphoria of the moment.

We stayed until the last out of the second game of doubleheaders, arriving home tired and sweaty. It meant that we didn't get home in time to go to the movies with my mother anymore. She accepted this with the same outward resignation with which she accepted everything my father did.

One extraordinarily hot Sunday afternoon as we prepared to leave the other house, my mother told us we were making a mistake, going out on "a day when the tongues were sticking out of dogs."

"The little one is delicate," she said. "He can't stand the heat the way you can."

"He can stand it," my father informed her. "He's been standing it every week."

"But it's never been as hot as today."

"It's not so hot," I said.

"What is it, cold?" she said irritably.

"Only a hundred and ten," my grandmother estimated. "What do you see in that idiocy? I could never understand *bessi-bolla*. Does it make you rich? Does it make you beautiful? It should make you fearful to see all those men behaving like mad dogs, attacking one another."

"Real games are different from what they played in the street," I explained.

"Why aren't all those louts in the Army?" my grandmother demanded.

"They're all either too young or too old or too sick," my father said, unbolting the front door. I heard Uncle Charlie chuckling on the cot.

"Crazy, you are both crazy," my mother yelled. "Don't you dare sit in the sun on a day like this."

I told her not to worry.

When we got off the subway at 167th Street to change for the shuttle to the Polo Grounds, my father asked me if I wanted to sit in the grandstand. "Maybe a doubleheader is too long to stay in the sun today," he said.

"No, that's all right," I answered. "I like it in the bleachers."

When we arrived back home, many hours later, our faces and arms were bright red and I felt dizzy.

"Holy Mother of God!" my mother exclaimed. "You sat in the sun! You are fools! You could have died! Your skin is the color of fire. You must be suffering the tortures of the damned."

"No," I lied. "It doesn't hurt."

THE AMERICAN

Once a month, Uncle Charlie rose two hours earlier than usual, washed his face, shaved, got dressed, and issued a call for pen and paper, materials which were in my custody. I'd fetch him a few sheets of the folded and ruled Woolworth stationery my father used, an envelope, a stamp, and, after filling it to capacity and checking it for mechanical defects, my second-best fountain pen. I arranged everything on the corner of the kitchen table where my grandfather had formerly sorted garlic, and stood back to watch the letter-writing ritual begin.

First, Uncle Charlie seated himself, lit a cigarette, and stared out at the fire escape. His cigarette finished, he got up, walked around the kitchen, returned to his chair, and put his head in his hands. Rising again, he went over to the sink and vigorously shook dandruff from his sparse hair. Then he washed and dried his hands, resumed his seat, and with lips pressed tightly around another cigarette, and eyes nearly shut against the smoke, took pen in hand to set down the date and salutation. At that point, he became even more serious. If my mother said something to him, he ignored her. If she accidently rattled pots and pans, he shushed her angrily. I would withdraw to our house, to await my mother's call to dinner, which I knew would be an hour or more late.

A week after each of his letters, Uncle Charlie got a reply from Georgia. He never told us what Barbara wrote. To my grandmother's regular question on the health of her grandson, he responded "Okay," and said no more.

Toward the end of July during the summer my father and I started going to ball games, however, Charlie volunteered that his son was coming to New York to see him.

"The barbarian is allowing it?" my grandmother asked.

"Allowing it? She had to. I told her to," Charlie said. "When I say something, she listens." He sounded elated.

My mother shook her head. "He's going to make that long trip alone?"

"He's old enough to take care of himself," Charlie said. "His mother will put him on the train and I'll meet him at the station. Is that hard?"

"Such a long train trip for a little boy by himself."

Charlie laughed. "Not everybody is as helpless as your sons. Not everybody brings up children to be afraid of their own shadow."

When Thomas Kenneth arrived two weeks later, he was taller and heavier than the last time I'd seen him. Nevertheless, my grandmother observed that he had languished down to nothing in his fatherless state. Charlie took a few days off, went out with his son daily, and, for the first time within my memory, slept at night.

On Sunday, my father suggested that the four of us go

to the ball game together. Charlie demurred when he found out my father was talking about a doubleheader at the Polo Grounds.

"If they were in the race, all right, but who wants to see the Giants this year?"

Thomas Kenneth said he did, because he'd never seen a real ball game. That settled the matter, although Charlie drew the line at sitting in the bleachers. My father bought four grandstand tickets.

Not only had Thomas Kenneth never seen a game, he seemed to have no idea of what baseball was all about. He became bored very quickly. His father, though he understood what was going on, wasn't having a much better time.

"Too slow, too dull, this game," he said. "Horse racing is the sport. It's fast and it's interesting when you've got money on it."

Father and son had their interest revived about the fifth inning, when a Giant batter lifted a high foul ball in our direction.

"I'll be dog," Thomas Kenneth shouted, jumping from his seat. "I think that ball's gonna land near here."

"Catch it, Tommy, catch it!" Charlie shouted. "Here it comes!"

My father remained seated, watching the ball's descent, while I cowered, afraid it would hit my glasses. Such a problem never arose in the bleachers, which were too far away to be reached by batted balls. All around us, other fans were standing and shoving one another.

The ball plummeted into the hands of a man two rows

in front of us and bounced out of them into the leaping, left-handed grasp of Thomas Kenneth. Whack!

"Attaboy, Tommy!" his father screamed. "Did you see that catch?" he yelled at us. "Boy, what a catch, what a catch!"

Thomas Kenneth was ecstatic for exactly half an inning, before he and his father lost interest again. We left the Polo Grounds at the end of the eighth inning of the first game.

On our way to the subway, Thomas Kenneth kept tossing the ball up, repeatedly re-enacting his catch.

"You going back to work tomorrow?" he asked his father.

"Yeah," Charlie sighed, emphasizing his distress. "I wish I could've taken the whole three weeks off but it can't be done. Listen, I had to sweat just to take off these few days. I ain't had this job too long, you know, so I can't do everything I'd like to. As long as I've got this job, I figure I'd better hold onto it. After all, you're still my responsibility. I still support you, you know. Every month, without fail, I mail your mother twenty dollars. Even when I wasn't working I did that, and it wasn't easy, believe me. Did she tell you that? Does she tell you about the money I send?"

"Oh, yeah, ah know," Thomas Kenneth said.

"Damn right. So that's why I have to go back tomorrow. I'll still see you, though. I mean, I don't have to go until seven o'clock, and I ain't gonna sleep all day. I can get along with less sleep. Then there's Saturday and Sunday. It'll be all right."

"Besides," said my father, touching my head lightly, "you got *this* Tommy to play with."

In the other house that night, Uncle Charlie's face started twitching when my father asked Thomas Kenneth about Barbara.

"I always liked your mother. She's got a good sense of humor. How's she doing down there?"

"Fine, just fine," Thomas Kenneth said.

"Is she working?"

"She's working in the mill in town," Thomas Kenneth answered. "She says all the time how she liked y'all a lot too. She was sorry she never did learn Eye-talian so's she could understand Granma and Aunt Santinny and Granpa. Ah'm sorry I didn't learn Eye-talian neither."

"You remember your grandfather?" Uncle Charlie asked proudly.

"Oh, yeah, sure I remember Granpa. I liked him a lot. I remember when he died, I cried."

"Well, maybe Granma and Granpa and Aunt Santina should have learned English," my father observed.

"I'll be dog." Thomas Kenneth shook his head. "I always did like every one of y'all. I wish ah could live up here again and my mother wasn't gonna get no divorce."

Charlie's face twitched some more. "Okay, that's enough," he said.

"You and Tommy will have a lot of fun the rest of your vacation, Tommy," my father said.

In bed that night, lying next to my cousin, I reminded him how he'd pointed out that we'd be having lots of good times as we grew older. He didn't recall the conversation but

agreed, just before falling asleep, that it would be nice to
go out together the next day, just the two of us. Perhaps
we could find a grassy place where we could toss his new
baseball around, he said. Thinking about that kept me
awake a long time.

After my father had left the next morning, I broached
the subject to my mother. Thomas Kenneth was still
asleep.

"Ma, *vulissimu nesceri*, we would like to go out."

"Who? Go out where?" she asked, disbelieving.

"Thomas Kenneth and I. I don't know, we would like to
take a walk, maybe, and find a place where we could throw
his ball around."

"That hard, heavy ball? You could kill someone with
that ball."

"We wouldn't throw it hard."

"No, not that ball."

"Well, maybe we could buy a rubber ball, then."

"No. Why don't you ever play ball inside any more, the
way you used to?"

"With his father asleep on the cot?"

"Play quietly, then."

"Maybe we could just take a walk and not play ball."

"Where? Where would you walk?"

"To the park, maybe."

"I'll take you to the park tonight, when your grandmother comes home."

"We could go to the movies, maybe, or even to the real
baseball game at the Polo Grounds."

167

"Later I'll take you both for a walk. I could take you to the Five and Ten."

"No, Ma, you and I went there day before yesterday."

"I know, but not with him. I could buy you something you could put together and play with nice and quiet."

"I think he just wants to go out with me," I said.

"No," my mother answered. "If the American wants to go out, let his father take him. You're not going out alone with him." She left for the other house, with the laundry.

I peeked in at Thomas Kenneth, who was just waking up.

"My mother won't let us go out," I told him.

He swung his legs over the side of the bed and yawned widely.

"You hear what I said? My mother won't let us go out."

"Is that right? I'll be dog."

After I watched him eat two fried eggs at the kitchen table in the other house, he went into the next room to wake up his father. There was a mumbled conversation, and Thomas Kenneth emerged with a pair of dollar bills. He looked at me questioningly.

"So we can't go out?" I asked my mother.

This time there was anger in her voice. "But what has come over you? All of a sudden, after twelve years, the blood is flowing to your head. Just like your father. What's the matter with you? One son is halfway around the world and the other suddenly wants to desert me. I've never had any trouble with you. I told you that if you want to go out together, I'll take you."

"We can't go," I translated for Thomas Kenneth.

168

"My father says I can go, Aunt Santinny," he said to my mother.

"You wanna go, you go. My Tommy, no. My Tommy stay hee."

"My father gave me money for the movies."

"*Lu pitchee,*" I said to my mother. "*Lu muvin pitchee.* It's just one block away on 116th Street. The one we went to with my father."

"No. You can't cross Third Avenue by yourself."

"We'd wait for the light."

"It's too dangerous. The cars that turn the corners are more dangerous than those that come straight. The ones that come straight stop at the light, certainly. But the ones that turn don't stop, and you can't see them coming."

"But if Tommy can do it why can't I?" I asked.

"The American is different. Everybody's different. The dentist, Connovi, says that each of us has a trumpet. Some play loudly, some play softly, some don't play the trumpet at all." She started to laugh, but it turned into a cough.

"Sicki," she explained to Thomas Kenneth. "Ima sicki." She spat into a handkerchief, and then began to move her lips, talking to herself.

"You go ahead," I told my cousin.

"It's no fun alone," he said.

"Tell him he'll meet plenty of loud trumpets like himself there and he can make friends," my mother said.

From the cot, Uncle Charlie yelled, "Go ahead, Tommy. Go to the movies by yourself. Tomorrow I'll get up early and take you wherever you wanna go. Right now I gotta get some sleep."

169

"Okay," Thomas Kenneth said, brightening. "I'll go after lunch. Let's play in your house now, Tommy."

"Okay," I said. "I'll teach you a baseball game you can play with dice."

During the rest of his stay, I saw my cousin mornings, evenings, and at meals. In the afternoons, he went out, mostly alone, a few times with his father. One hot night, a day or two before he returned to Georgia, we were looking out together from one of the front-room windows of the other house at the children of 117th Street playing by an open fire hydrant. Someone had placed a bottomless garbage can on it, sending water high into the air. We could feel some drops even where we were.

"I'd like to go down there," Thomas Kenneth said.

"We could play waterfall in the kitchen," I suggested. "Come on."

I asked my mother for a milk bottle cap, wedged it into the faucet, and turned on the cold water. My cousin marveled at the fine, chilling spray.

"Only wet your wrists," my mother cautioned, "and not for too long."

"Are they getting the floor wet?" my grandmother asked, not looking up from her cutaways.

My mother told her we weren't. "It *is* hot," she said. "Refresh yourselves."

Thomas Kenneth tilted the bottle cap to aim a watery salvo at a cockroach under the soap dish. It fell into the sink, drowned, and disappeared down the drain.

"Wow, did you see that?"

"Yeah, yeah," I said, as excited as he.

"Oh, oh, here comes another one." He removed the bottle cap and produced an even more forceful blast using a forefinger. Direct hit! We cheered.

"*Atti, chi fasciti?* What are you doing?" my grandmother hollered.

"That's enough now," said my mother.

"Just a little more," I said.

"All right, but play nice."

"You know what?" I said to Thomas Kenneth. "This must be Coney Island and we must be lifeguards."

"And try to save the cockroaches? I'll be dog!"

My mother understood "Coney Island."

"*Conniale?*" she said. "We used to go to *Conniale*, your father and I, before you were born." She laughed and came to wet her wrists under the faucet.

THE SNOWBALL

The first day of my second year at Galvani was marked by another painful hallway incident. Zircon Roon, who was again in my home room, had been sauntering ahead of me, when a bigger boy ran by, knocking his books down. Roon cursed loudly and looked menacingly after the runner, but did not chase him. Seeing me, he muttered something I didn't understand and then yelled, "Hey Martin, you want to write my book reports this year?"

That he should speak to me was startling enough, but this proposal was so unexpected that I could think of no answer.

"What's the matter?" he glared. "Why don't you pick up my books?"

I started to walk away, but his hand on my shoulder whirled me around. "Answer when I talk to you."

He grabbed the knot of my necktie, shoving his knuckles into my throat. "Little ginny stinker still wears knickers and his mother takes him to school."

I was filled with an alarm that made my eyes sting, and an anger I'd never felt before.

"Let go my tie," I said, dropping my books. I grabbed his fist with my right hand and pushed hard against his chest with my left, knocking him off balance into the wall. The action surprised me as much as it did Roon.

"Take off your glasses," he challenged, coming at me.

I tried another push, but he'd already grabbed me and was trying to wrestle me to the floor. I held on to him tightly and didn't fall. Suddenly, he pushed me hard through the open doors on the stair landing, sending me whirling backwards. I grabbed desperately with both hands at the railing, and caught it. I skidded several steps but kept my feet. When I straightened up, Roon was still standing on the landing, looking mean. I turned away and walked down the rest of the flight to the turn-off, where I looked up again through cloudy glasses. Roon was still there, making no effort to follow. A few boys looked on curiously, but nobody said, "Hit him again," or "Break his ass" —cries I'd heard addressed to student combatants in the past. I adjusted my clothes and walked back up the stairs.

"Don't forget your books," Roon said as I passed him.

I had managed to compose myself by noon when my mother called for me, but after lunch, in the home room, I avoided looking at Roon. At the end of the day, as I was returning there, I felt a tap on my shoulder and turned to face my antagonist.

"Did I hurt you?" he asked.

I shook my head.

"Are you going to stay away from The Boys' Club again all year?"

Once more, he'd asked me an unexpected question to

which I could not respond immediately. This time he did not react angrily. Instead he said: "Look, what you did last year was stupid. You could check in at the club and then sneak out. That's what I did."

"But you stayed the first day," I said, not looking him in the eye. "You pitched in the boxball game."

"I did? Well, I probably stuck around there a few times in the beginning. But after that, I only hung around till they called the roll. Ain't you ever cut a class? I done that plenty, not just with The Boys' Club. It's easier with The Boys' Club, though, and you even get marked present. And this year it's gonna be even easier. You don't even have to go back to school after. That's the way they do when Boys' Club is the last period. They dismiss you right there. There's a lot you can get away with if you know how. How come you got promoted with all those absences anyway?"

"I didn't even fail in Physical Education," I smiled. "They marked me 'incomplete' the first term, and nothing the second term."

"Boy, are they screwed up," laughed Zircon Roon.

That night, I tried to explain about The Boys' Club to my mother.

"It's better that you stay home like last year," she said.

"But this time they might catch on and fail me. This way, they'll think I'm there."

"It would mean I'd have to pick you up at this place. What time should I come?"

"I don't know. We're supposed to be there at five to two, and the boy said we can get out a few minutes after that. But I think I could come home by myself with him."

"Who is he? Can he be trusted? Where does he live?"

"He's a good boy and he lives around here."

"No, I don't like it. I'll be in front of The Boys' Club at two o'clock and wait for you. It would be better still if you stayed home again."

Friday morning, I insisted on going to school, leaving open the question of whether I'd go back in the afternoon. When Roon asked me if I was ready to go to The Boys' Club, I said I was. I so informed my mother at lunchtime. She seemed strangely detached, and finally said that it wouldn't be worthwhile for her to go home after she took me back to Galvani for the afternoon.

"I'd hardly get home when it would be time to turn around and go back to get you at this *boisi clubbu.*"

"That's right. So why don't you let me come home alone? I mean, with this boy."

"No, no. I'll go into some stores, and be in front of *lu boisi clubbu* at two o'clock. It's that building on 111th Street that we pass when we go to the sepulcher at St. Anne's, isn't it?"

I nodded glumly.

Mr. Ramsey, our new home room teacher, led us on the two-block walk from school to the club a few minutes before two. When we reached the corner of 111th Street, I glimpsed my mother already standing in front of the building, and turned away.

"Your mother's here," Roon said sharply. "What's wrong with her?"

"What do you mean?"

"Well, look at her. She's talking to herself."

I saw her working her jaws and moving her lips again.

She stopped when she picked me out of line, smiled, and made motions with her hands to tell me she'd wait.

Less than ten minutes later, I was at her side. It had been as easy as Roon had said. A paunchy, middle-aged man had lined us up, called the roll, blown a whistle, and Roon and I had made our way amid a confusion of running boys and bouncing basketballs to a water fountain near the exit. We drank and slipped out.

"I'm going to walk over by the river," Roon had said.

"Okay, see you Monday."

My mother was calm on our way back home. She'd seen Roon accompanying me and she said he looked like a nice boy. "Small, like you."

I told her that, in the future, it would take us a little longer to get out because we were going to have to change into our gym clothes before attendance was checked, and, naturally, we'd have to change back into street clothes before leaving the building.

"So much trouble. I still think it would be better if you just stayed home."

"No, it's better this way. The days we're supposed to swim we don't have to put on our gym clothes at all. We just go naked to the pool. My friend says it's just as easy to sneak out of there."

"Naked? Mother of God, have they no shame in this land?"

"But it's good because we won't waste so much time putting on and taking off our gym clothes on those days."

"But naked! You'll catch cold."

"The place is very hot. Don't worry."

"What are these gym clothes you're supposed to have?"

"Just a pair of short pants and something for . . . between the . . . it's something to protect the biscuit. It's called a *jocku strappa*."

She shook her head. "America! The dawn came and we discovered America."

"I'll need a lock, too. Everybody has to have a locker where they keep their clothes."

"Yes, yes," she recalled. "I remember now. Your brother had them in Newark. He broke his foot once in that cursed *gymmu*."

"He didn't really break it, he just sprained an ankle."

"Whatever it was, he couldn't walk without screaming for six months. I think we still have his lock. His pants wouldn't fit you, though. Neither would his . . . What filth is America!"

The shorts my mother bought, though one or two sizes too large, managed to stay up for the few minutes I needed them. Underneath I wore a pair of jockey shorts she'd bought as a compromise jock strap. I felt indecently exposed the first time I wore this garb, and even worse the first time I had to walk naked to the pool. But when I saw that no one even looked at me, it soon became routine.

During the many weeks we sneaked out of The Boys' Club, neither Zircon Roon nor I ever mentioned the altercation that had brought us together. He said no more about my writing book reports for him, either. In fact, we didn't talk much about anything. For me, the bond between us had been formed in fear, hostility, and the desire not to offend, much in the same way that I had first consented to accompany my father to baseball games.

But it was a different kind of desire that made me accept Roon's offer of a packet of twelve "dirty pictures" for a dollar. A glimpse of the top photograph was enough. It was of a nude woman holding an enormous fishing pole, standing by the edge of a stream. Not even the *French Femmes* had looked so naughty, and Roon assured me that the other eleven views were even better. I told him I had no idea how I could get a dollar from my mother without explaining what I needed it for. He suggested I steal it from her purse. After several days of inner turmoil, I did. I kept the pictures in their original brown paper bag, on the ledge in our *beckowzu*, where I knew they would remain undisturbed. After dinner every night, I'd go over to our side of the hall to look at them. I told Roon that if ever he had any more such merchandise, he had a customer.

By that time, I was calling Zircon Roon "Tex." When he first told me I should call him that, I expressed respectful curiosity. Hadn't he said his parents were from South Carolina? He replied that "Tex" was what he liked to be called, and all his friends and even his parents respected his wishes. He continued to call me "Martin."

It wasn't until a snowy day in December that Tex and I cut something besides The Boys' Club together. It was a math class we both hated which came first thing after home room three mornings a week. When he proposed the idea, I objected apprehensively.

"But where will we go?"

"We'll fool around in the snow outside."

"The snow? It's too cold and our coats are in the home

room. Besides, how are we going to get out of the building?"

Tex laughed and parroted, "Our coats are in the home room. So who's in the home room the first period Wednesday morning?"

"I don't know."

"Nobody, that's who."

"But don't they lock the door?"

Tex clucked his tongue. "No, they *don't* lock the door, stupid. I mean, there's no class in there, but Ramsey's there, marking papers. He's got a free first period every Wednesday."

I marveled at the extent of his knowledge, but still couldn't understand how we could get our coats if our teacher was in the room. Tex said he would show me. My mother would have been aghast had she known I was considering going out in the snow. But if I didn't go with Tex, I might never have another friend.

"How will we get out of the building?" I asked again.

"Just leave that part to me. You coming?"

I nodded.

Tex strolled to the end of the hall with me at his side, turned and signaled me to retrace our steps. By the time we reached our home room door, the hall was quiet. The door was open and Mr. Ramsey was bending over his desk. Tex walked in boldly. I followed with my head down.

Our teacher looked up. "Yes, boys?"

"We're getting our coats. I'm cold, teach, and so's Martin."

Mr. Ramsey smiled and nodded.

"Real hard, wasn't it?" Tex asked me sarcastically in the hall.

"I don't understand why he believed you. The steam is on full blast."

"There's plenty you don't understand, Martin. Ramsey don't care. He just don't want no trouble, that's all."

"But if you knew you were going to cut the class, why didn't you walk out with your coat when we left the home room a few minutes ago?"

"I couldna done it then. He woulda stopped me. You ain't supposed to walk out of your home room with your coat."

I shook my head, not understanding again.

"Not in front of the whole class, dope. He couldna let me do that. Besides, I wasn't sure then I was gonna cut this class."

We finished buttoning our coats in a stairwell. Mine was an enormous woolly brown one that reached almost to my ankles. My companion's was what my mother would have called a *lumbejechi*. I lowered the earflaps on my cap and followed Tex down to the basement. We crossed it and arrived at another, narrower, stairway. When he pushed open the door at its top, I was surprised to find that we were in back of the school. Tex instantly ran ahead across the street, wriggled through a hole in a wire fence into a vacant lot, and started grabbing chunks of snow barehanded. I took my woolen gloves from my coat pocket and, realizing I'd left my galoshes in the closet—another cause for consternation had my mother known—walked to the corner. I waited for the light before crossing.

The Snowball

The snow was already much deeper than it had been when my mother had dropped me off half an hour earlier. Had it been snowing as hard then, she probably would not have taken me to school at all. Snow got into my shoes as I pushed my way clumsily through the hole in the fence. Inside the lot, I waited for whatever was going to happen next.

Tex had amassed a supply of snowballs which he now proceeded to throw at passing cars and pedestrians, hitting neither.

"Ain't you gonna make snowballs?" he asked.

"Yeah, later." My nose was starting to run.

"Whatsa matter, you cold?"

"A little," I admitted.

"You ack like you never played in the snow before."

"Oh, sure, Tex, I played in the snow." I stooped to pick some up and formed it into a ball.

"Attaboy, Martin. Now throw it."

I threw it blindly, as hard as I could. Across the street, two women were walking by the school. All I could tell through my wet glasses was that one was carrying an umbrella and was considerably older than the other. The younger one could have been a high school girl. The only thing I was sure of was that she was wearing a green kerchief, and a second later my snowball splattered against it.

"Holy shit!" Tex shouted. "What a shot! Man, and I thought you never played in the snow before. Holy shit!"

The woman holding the umbrella screamed at us from across the street. "No good bums! Spick bastids!"

"Heh. She thinks we're spicks. Holy shit, the girl is putting her hand under her kerchief to feel if she's still got an ear. You gave her some smash, Martin."

As the women moved away, I smiled weakly and made some more snowballs. "I'll make 'em and you throw 'em, Tex," I said.

I thought I would perish of cold and remorse before Tex signaled that it was time for us to return to school.

At noon my mother was waiting in front of the school, her black coat covered with snow and her umbrella bending in the wind.

At home, I told her that, despite my galoshes, I'd gotten my feet wet on the way. She hurried to get me another pair of socks.

"You're not going to school after lunch," she said, coughing. "We're not going to die of pneumonia in this tempest."

I spent most of the afternoon by the pot-bellied stove in our house listening to the radio and occasionally going into *lu beckowzu* to look at the photographs Tex had sold me. I thought a lot about the girl I'd hit. Perhaps she'd been sick and that was why she hadn't been in school. But in that case, she wouldn't have been out in such bad weather. Maybe there was something wrong with her mind. She could have been mentally retarded or something. It could be, of course, that she wasn't a schoolgirl at all, but a small woman. Or it could be that she was a schoolgirl and her mother had been keeping her away from The Girls' Club. They could have been on their way to the doctor for a note.

THE CESSPOOL

One afternoon, after reading the news, WOV announcer Guido Lupavelli dulcetly advised his *cari ascoltatori* and *care ascoltatrice*, his dear male and female listeners, that one of his dear sponsors, the Fioravanti Macaroni Company, would send them a lovely holy calendar free for the asking.

"And let us hope that all the great saints depicted on its pages, as well as the Sacred Heart of Jesus and the Immaculate Heart of Mary which you will also see in beautiful, artistic colors, will be moved to grant that this coming *Anno Domini* of one thousand, nine hundred and forty-five will at last welcome a restoration of peace and tranquillity to our long-suffering world."

"Could you write him a letter for me?" my mother asked.

One letter more or less didn't bother the official family scribe any, but I was curious why she wanted me to write in English.

"I can't write *real* Italian," she explained. "Guido Lupavelli would laugh at my *grammatica*. One doesn't

183

write in Sicilian to such a person. Educated people like that understand English, so you write to him as elegantly as you can."

I wrote: "Dear Mr. Lupavelli, Please send me the calendar of the Fioravanti Macaroni Company which you mentioned in your radio broadcast. Thanking you in advance, I am, Yours truly, Santina Martana."

"What did you write?" my mother wanted to know.

I started translating for her. "*Caro Signor Lupavelli . . .*"

"*Caro?*" my mother interrupted. "Isn't that too affectionate? After all, I don't know the man. Should a married woman writing to a strange man address him as *Caro?*" She smiled and coughed.

"It isn't a matter of affection," I assured her. "There's nothing affectionate about it. That's just the way you begin a letter or a card in English. But if you want, I can say 'My dear Mr. Lupavelli.' That's more formal."

"What's the difference? What does it mean?"

"*Mio caro.*"

"Heaven forbid! That's entirely too forward. That's the way one addresses a lover."

I convinced her to send off the note as written, and in two weeks we had our calendar. In addition to the saints and divine hearts Guido Lupavelli had mentioned, there was a gory illustration, for November, of the tormented souls in Purgatory. My mother was quite pleased and hung the calendar on the inside of the front door in our house.

Increasingly in these days her lips moved, her eyes darted, and she looked like a tormented soul herself. When I'd ask what the matter was, her movements would stop, and she'd assure me that nothing was wrong. Physically, her cough had subsided, but she suffered regularly with pains in her limbs. Her gums were empty, awaiting a full set of dentures.

The Saturday she got her teeth, she sat at the kitchen table smiling pitifully and, I imagine, painfully. She lisped that the teeth were too large, that Dr. Connovi had got her size wrong.

The next day, my father told her she'd get used to them, and assured her that she looked very well. But by Sunday night, she'd removed them.

"Oh, my heart came back," she said. "I was suffering the tortures of hell."

My father warned her that the longer she kept them out, the longer it would take her to get used to them.

"It will only hurt for a few more days, and then you won't know any more that you have false teeth," he said.

"In Camporeale, plenty of people got along very well without teeth," my mother answered. "Remember Betta the Hairy-Legged? She could chew walnuts with her gums." Turning to my grandmother, she added, "*La confettara* in the park has no teeth either."

"You are younger than was Betta the Hairy-Legged, and I'm sure you are younger than the woman in the park," my father said. "You are too young not to have teeth."

"You spent over two hundred dollars for them," my grandmother said, "and went through all the pain of pulling. You should wear them. Though, personally, I am very happy with the four wobbly teeth I have left."

"Young?" my mother said deprecatingly. "The change has come. Is it true men change, too?" she asked slyly.

"That's what they say," my father replied. "I don't see any sign of it myself."

"It will come to the Standard Bearer as it has to his wife," my mother laughed. "You won't have any teeth left either."

My father reminded her that he had few of his own already. He told her again how he'd had eight pulled at one sitting, had gone to work the same afternoon, but had been sent home when his boss noticed blood around his mouth. Within a week, he said, he'd had his dentures in place.

"Of course it was hard getting used to them. But if I'd kept taking them out, I'd never have gotten used to them at all. You just have to make up your mind to endure the pain for a while."

"My trumpet is softer than yours," my mother said. "Those horse teeth stay in the drawer."

Shortly after she'd put her teeth in the drawer, never to take them out again, my mother astonished me one morning when, upon arising to get ready for school, I found her in our kitchen, wreathed in smoke.

"You're smoking a cigarette!" I exclaimed redundantly.

She was grinning, whether in pleasure or embarrassment I didn't know. All I knew was that I was embarrassed. I wondered what her mother would say. What would my father say? What did she mean, upsetting me like this so early in the morning? What was coming over her lately, anyhow?

"I felt like smoking," she said. "Your father smokes,

your brother smokes. Your uncles smoke, and your aunt smokes. Now my life has changed and I want to smoke. I *have* to smoke. I've been told to."

I asked her who had told her to do such a thing.

"You know nothing about your mother," she answered. "You know nothing of her greatness. Your mother talks to Saints. Now wash your face. Let's not be late for school."

She took frequent puffs, without inhaling. I heard the door of the other house open and close. My grandmother's voice said, "Santina, I'm going."

"Very well," my mother shouted back, expelling smoke furiously. Less loudly, she added, "And may a dynamite charge split your head open before you come back, evil old woman."

Was that the kind of remark she'd been making soundlessly until this morning?

"*Andiamo,*" my mother urged, after my grandmother's footsteps had faded down the stairs. She extinguished her cigarette by throwing it in the sink and accompanied me to the other house. As soon as we were there, she extracted a pack from the pocket of her housedress and lit another cigarette. They were the same wartime brand my father smoked.

I hoped Uncle Charlie wouldn't have to go to the *beckowzu,* but I knew Aunt Pina would be getting up before we left for school to get ready to go to her job in a neighborhood drug store, work she'd obtained through the good offices of Dr. Gaione. When she did get up, my mother was smoking her fifth cigarette of the morning, while I was trying to drink my coffee and egg.

Pina regarded the whole thing as a joke. She kept staring at my mother and laughing.

"This is America," my mother said, "where everybody smokes. It clears my head. I had such a weight on my head, a weight I've had for years. The weight lifted with my first puff."

"Does our mother know?" Pina asked uproariously. "And what about your husband and," she motioned to the next room, "your brother?" She was laughing so loudly I thought Charlie would wake up for sure.

My mother made it clear she did not care about the family's reaction. "The change of life is to blame. I must smoke for my health. I have been told to."

On our way to school, I was thankful that my mother didn't smoke on the street.

The reactions of the rest of the family weren't as hostile as I'd feared. My grandmother, after protesting that her mother would never have allowed such a thing, was silenced when my mother reminded her about Pina. Uncle Charlie's reaction was nearly as jovial as Pina's. He told my mother that, if she really wanted to smoke, she ought to smoke Camels, as he did. She took one, and immediately pronounced it "too strong." Charlie laughed, pointing out that, since she hadn't inhaled, she had no way of knowing how strong it was. My father, while hoping that my mother's smoking betokened a belated Americanization, was alarmed at how much she smoked. She smoked continuously, from the time she got up to the time she went to bed, pausing only for meals and for going out. My father wondered whether the smoking wouldn't bring back her cough.

"And if you were going to start smoking, why the hell didn't you wait till the war was over?" he chuckled. "What do you do, stand on line for cigarettes?"

My mother said she didn't mind. "I have plenty of time to stand on line on Friday afternoons waiting for Tommy to come out of *lu boisi clubbu*."

"I offered to get her Camels," Uncle Charlie chimed in. "I could get 'em for you, too, with my connections. You used to smoke Camels."

"Never mind," my father said. "Those cigarettes are for the soldiers, not for you and me."

One soldier in the family was about to leave high quality cigarettes behind.

"Vito Marcantonio has succeeded," my grandmother announced jubilantly one Sunday morning when she returned from Aunt Concetta's. "He's getting Nick out of the Army." She was shaking with vindicated righteousness. "The politician," she said, "told those captains and generals that my son is the father of two sick children and the husband of a sick and penniless wife. 'He is needed at home,' he told them."

"Are Concetta and the children sick?" I asked.

"This is what Marcantonio told them," my grandmother said confidentially, "and he had the doctors' certificates to prove it."

But by the time my uncle arrived back in East Harlem, our happiness had been dampened by my mother's continued strange behavior.

189

I was turning on the radio in our kitchen one night when she shrieked, "Turn off that cesspool! If you want to listen to that cesspool do it in the other house. What did you write to that man? I told you 'caro' was too affectionate. Now they are making fun of me."

I told her I didn't understand what she was talking about.

"They are making fun of me on the cesspool all day long, that son of a slut, Guido Lupavelli, and that whore, and all those peasants. All day long they talk about me. 'What brazen woman would dare address a strange man as caro,' they say, and they laugh. They take me for a whore like them."

The next morning, my mother's loud talking awakened me long before the usual time. She was still in her nightgown, standing in the middle of the kitchen. She was not smoking, but trembling, and incoherently cursing Saint Anthony. Her face was bright red, and tears were streaming down her cheeks. The calendar Guido Lupavelli had sent us was on the floor, torn into small pieces.

"Ma, Ma," I cried, but she paid no attention.

I'd never heard her voice like that before. It was rumbling out of her in a hoarse croak, loud enough to be heard in the other house.

"It's true, it's true," she repeated over and over, "they want to kill me. Assassins! Devils! It's true. The old woman and the Snipped Biscuit. Guido Lupavelli was Paoluccio and now he is il dottore Gaione. Dottore Gaione, Gaione, garzone, assassino. He played on her. True, true. St. Anthony, I asked you to help me, but I should have known you were in league with them, and a devil yourself. A devil and an assassin too. Jesus Christ an assassin too. The Virgin is a whore and St. Joseph is a cuckold. Guido Lupavelli, *cari ascoltatori e care ascoltatrice*. Cuckolding bastard!"

She croaked on, not in Sicilian, but in perfect Italian, as on the radio.

I threw my arms around her, saying, "Ma, Ma, what is it? Calm yourself. You're scaring me." But she kept croaking while I clung to her, until my grandmother opened our door with her key, pried me loose, and told me to go into the other house and stay there.

Uncle Charlie and Aunt Pina, also aroused by the commotion, asked me what was going on. I told them my mother was talking wildly, as though she'd gone crazy.

"I knew it," Charlie said. "I've been noticing something going wrong with that woman. She keeps this kid cooped up all his life, all of a sudden she starts talking to herself, she starts smoking . . . at her age, it ain't normal. If you ask me, I don't think she ever was normal. I said something like this was bound to happen. Didn't I say something like this was gonna happen?" he asked Pina.

"I don't know if you said it," she answered, "but what are we standing here for? Let's see what's the matter with her. She might need an ambulance. She might hurt herself or the old lady, you never know in these things. What's your grandmother doing with her?" Pina asked me.

I told her I didn't know. My mother's voice still rumbled across the hall.

"You stay here, kid. We're going over there."

Uncle Charlie followed Pina, and I was alone. I tried pretending that soon my mother would call out that it was time for me to get up and get ready for school, but I knew this was no dream. That was my mother's voice I was hearing now, no matter how strange it sounded. I threw myself on Charlie's cot, trying to drown it out. Soon I succeeded, with the sound of my own sobs.

My uncle was the first one back. He found me still lying on his cot, but I was calmer. The sounds from next door seemed to have quieted, too.

"Ahh, it's nothing," he said. "She'll be all right. She was a little upset but she's quieting down now. Listen, Tommy, you know what's the name of the place your father works?"

Of course I knew the name. So should he.

"Kreiner's," I said.

"Where's that, in Newark?"

I nodded.

"Would he be there now? No, he wouldn't be there now, it's too early," my uncle answered his own question. "Listen, would you happen to know where he lives over there, the address of his room?"

I told him we had it written in a memo pad which was in a bureau across the hall.

"Okay, good. Could you get it? Pina wants to call him and call the doctor, too."

I asked my uncle if I could go across the hall now.

"Sure, sure. She's all right now. Everything's okay. She's sitting down nice and easy."

When I got there, Pina said sharply, "Tommy, stay across the hall."

The Cesspool

"I came to get my father's address," I said. My mother was seated quietly, resting her elbows on our kitchen table. She was supporting her cheek with her left hand, and in the hand was a cigarette with a long, curved ash. As I watched, my grandmother took the cigarette and snuffed it out in a circular ashtray which said "Kreiner's" around its circumference. Methodically, my mother lit another.

"Those Godforsaken cigarettes," my grandmother said.

I went to the drawer of my mother's bureau where I knew my father's address was, got the waiter's check pad my father used as a memo book, and gave it to my aunt.

"Good, there's the phone number, too," she said. "Your father's got a phone in his room?"

"I think it's probably his boss's," I said. "They live in the same building."

"Where's that, in Newark?"

"Of course it's in Newark," I said.

"Okay, kid, come on back to the other house now. I'm gonna throw on some clothes and go down to the candy store to make these calls. I'm calling Dr. Gaione, too, all right?"

"I don't know. She was just cursing him, but I guess you'd better call him."

She asked my grandmother if it was all right to leave her alone with my mother.

"Do me a favor," my grandmother said. "Make a telephone call to *Li Roggispiti* while you're at it. Tell them I'll be late."

"For God's sake, it's early yet. There's probably nobody there."

An hour later I was seated at the kitchen table in the other house, listening to my uncle Charlie's snores, when there was a knock at the door. My grandmother and Pina must have heard it too, for they were opening the door to our house as I opened the door of the other house. Dr. Gaione pirouetted uncertainly before entering the correct one. I asked Pina if I could come in too, but she told me I'd better stay put. I shut the door, locked it with all four locks, and walked past my sleeping uncle into the front room. I stayed there until there was another knock.

"How come you locked the door?" Pina said. "Your mother wants to know if you've had your coffee and egg yet."

I darted by her and into our house. My mother was still sitting in the same place, while my grandmother shoveled coal into our pot-bellied stove. There was no sign of Dr. Gaione.

"*Chi si dice?*" I asked my mother. "What do you say?"

Her voice was as expressionless as the eyes she turned on me. "Ay, my son. No school today. Did they make you your coffee?"

I shook my head. "I don't want any."

"I'll make it, I'll make it," my grandmother volunteered.

"Tommy, see if there are any more cigarettes in the bedroom," my mother said.

"You should go to bed now," recommended my grandmother, "never mind the cigarettes."

"Very well," my mother replied, "as you say. You say I'm crazy." She got up slowly and moved unsteadily toward her bedroom.

194

"*Gaetaneddu*, you want egg in your coffee?" my grandmother asked.

Wasn't that the way I'd always had it? I nodded and asked her what the doctor had said.

"Nothing, nothing. It's all right."

I turned to my aunt.

"He thinks she might have to have some treatments," Pina said. "First he wants another doctor to look at her, a psychiatrist. He's gotta find one who speaks Italian, naturally."

"Tommy," my mother called in a thin, tired voice. I hurried to her bed, followed by my grandmother and Pina. In her bedroom I could feel the cold air seeping in from under the yellow curtain.

"Not you," my mother said, more firmly, to my grandmother and Pina. "I want to talk to my son only."

"Very well," my grandmother said to me, "stay with your mother until I call you for the coffee."

Pina advised me she'd be in our kitchen in case I needed her.

"No, you go, too. Go to the other house," my mother ordered.

"Don't drink it," she said when we were alone.

"What?"

"Don't drink the coffee and egg. I'll make it for you later. She is an evil woman and so is her daughter. They put poison and ground glass in my food."

"But you do the cooking."

"They have ways, my son. You are too innocent to understand these things."

"What was the matter this morning?" I asked.

"I was disgusted with it all. They were going too far. But God will punish them. We shall see who is rewarded and who is damned on the Day of Judgment. Did they call Snipped Biscuit?"

I nodded.

"Certainly. The accomplice. The lover. What did he say?"

I told her I hadn't found out yet.

"He'll surely be here soon, to be with his whores. I must warn you now, my son. Come closer."

I knelt by the bed.

"Say nothing of this to your brother. We mustn't worry him. If I'm still alive when he comes back, I will tell him all I am about to tell you now. In the meantime, continue to write to him as though nothing had happened. Do you promise?"

I said I did, but that she should not talk of dying. She smiled and told me not to worry.

"Great things are happening to your mother, divine things which that devil, Guido Lupavelli, tried to prevent. God will punish him. They gave me poisonous powders, those evil women. From when I was a little girl, that woman has been trying to poison me. When I was five and sick with the fevers, she used to give me some of her poison pills. But I fooled her. Every morning I took her pill down to the dump with the chamberpots. And she thought I had already taken it. Ha, *bella fu!* She couldn't understand why I was taking so long to die. One must be wise to survive. Now she has her daughter in league with her, trying to poison me. Let me tell you about your father now. Your father is her *garzu*, her lover."

"What do you mean? Whose lover?"

"Both! How do you think your aunt was born? He put his snipped biscuit into that old slut and that was the result. Now he enjoys them both."

"Oh, Ma, you're not making any sense." I felt I was going to cry again.

"Quiet and listen!" she commanded. She rolled her eyes upward and said, "He doesn't believe me. My own son doesn't believe me. They have turned him against me. As I feared, he takes after his father. That bastard Guido Lupavelli."

"What has Guido Lupavelli got to do with it?"

"He talks about me on that cesspool your father brought into the house. I liked Guido Lupavelli. I fell in love with his voice. Did you hear my voice this morning? Masculine and heavy, like Guido Lupavelli's. But I didn't want to call him 'dear.' You did that."

She paused accusingly, but when I said nothing, she continued.

"There was a boy back in Camporeale named Paoluccio. The third time my father took us back . . . what was I, sixteen? Paoluccio was dying. And I said to that slut, '*Madre mia, madre bella,* I want to go see Paoluccio.' 'Never mind,' she told me, 'you'll go tomorrow.' I had a premonition that Paoluccio was dying, but that evil woman refused to let me go. Now Paoluccio's soul haunts me."

I'd never heard my mother mention this name before. Of all the things she'd said that morning, this avowal of a childhood sweetheart seemed to me the most surprising thing of all.

"First the soul of Paoluccio went into the soul of Guido Lupavelli. Two years ago, at the Feast of Mount Carmel, I saw a distinguished gentleman passing by and I knew that he was Guido Lupavelli-Paoluccio. He had taken over the body, you see. Do you understand me?"

"Yes, but it makes no sense."

"Never mind. Why are you crying? Stop crying and listen, just listen so that someday you can tell your mother's story to the world. What a story it will make. 'Santa, she was a saint, indeed,' people will say. But Guido Lupavelli was not worthy of having Paoluccio's soul in his body, nor was he worthy of being the father of the new Saviour. For I had been chosen, my son. An angel came to me while I was awake and told me that great things would happen in my womb. But Guido Lupavelli blasphemed. He made fun of me. And Paoluccio's soul found a new haven. Do you know where? In *il dottore* Gaione! Yes, *il dottore* Gaione."

"Dr. Gaione is now Paoluccio? How could it be? Can't you understand how impossible what you're saying is?"

"Quiet! Attention! Attention!" she shouted, just as my grandmother arrived to announce my coffee.

"He'll be there soon," my mother yelled, "get out of here."

"Calm yourself," I said.

"All right, the coffee is on the table," my grandmother said. "I'm going to work now, Santa. Your husband will be here soon." She pulled our door shut behind her.

"Go, whore, go," my mother called after her. "All her life she's gone away and left me to do everything, cook and clean and bring up her children for her. I was old before I was ten. But her husband pronounced the appropriate sentence and she will end up on the Bowery with the rest. It was the slut who took Dr. Gaione away from me. The doctor came to see me and your aunt-sister took him away. Now she is plotting with her mother and her father-lover to get me out of the way. But I shall be vindicated when the Saviour is born. Let them plot now. We will see who will triumph at the Judgment."

I held my mother's hand as she talked on of these weird things. I felt futile, trying to comfort the woman who had always comforted me. At length she closed her eyes and, opening them a minute or two later, said, "You will go to school tomorrow. I will take you. I feel much better now that I have told my son of all the evil his mother has had to face."

The front door opened and Aunt Pina called out, "Tommy, everything all right? Your coffee's cold already."

My mother tensed and shouted back, "I'll make my son his coffee. Get out of my house." My aunt retreated immediately.

"Why was the door open?" my mother demanded. "So any villain or slut can walk in to do their evil work? Go lock it right now. You're not drinking any of their poison."

I arose with a brittle snap of my legs to go and lock the door. My mother bounded out of bed to follow.

"They're not coming here again, mother or daughter," she said. "And I'm not going over there. My years of servitude to the old woman are over. Let her cook her poison and ground glass for herself when she comes home. I don't need that house. I have my own house here."

She flung open the door of the kitchen closet, rattling the pots.

"I cook only for my son from now on, and for myself. I don't need them any more. It is ended."

She took out an old coffeepot I hadn't seen since Newark and began polishing it vigorously. When she'd finished, she slammed it angrily on the range.

"Tommy, go to the other house and get the can of coffee and an egg."

The door to the other house was unlocked. I found Pina fussing with her hair before the big mirror between the kitchen windows.

"Why'd she yell at me like that?" my aunt asked me.

"I don't know. She's not responsible for what she's saying."

"I always liked her. I always treated her with respect. After all, the woman's my sister."

"You can't take what she said seriously," I said. "She's sick and she's not making sense. Like, she said you and grandma tried to poison her."

Pina was shocked. "What? I've always been so good to her. Why the hell should she think something like that? Even when I was dead drunk, I never did anything to hurt her. And my poor mother—there's nothing she wouldn't do for her. Nothing's ever been too good for her precious Santina."

"I know, I know. Is my father coming?"

"He oughta be here soon. The poor man was sleeping. They hadda go and wake him up. What kind of place is it he lives in, anyhow, a rooming house?"

I said I didn't know for sure. I wished my father would arrive soon.

"Drink your coffee," Pina said, pointing to the cup on the table. "If it's too cold, I'll heat it up for you."

"No, that's all right." I gulped it down and went to the icebox for an egg. My aunt asked me what I was doing.

"She wants to have some coffee and egg," I said.

"Oh, that's a good sign. I'll make it for her."

"She wants to do it herself."

"Tommy!" My mother's call had that croak again. "Tommy, Tommy!"

"Where's the coffee can?" I asked my aunt.

"Over there on the washtub."

"Okay, I'm going back."

"You want me to come with you?"

"No. Wait, maybe I better take more eggs."

I returned to the icebox and got a full carton.

"Tommy! Tommy!"

I ran across the hall clutching the coffee can and the eggs, trying to keep the coffee and egg I'd already drunk down in my stomach. My mother, red-faced and sweating, asked why I'd taken so long. Had I been talking to the whore? But when she saw I'd brought a whole dozen eggs, she calmed down.

"*Bravo*, you behaved as a true son. There's no reason to go back now." I wondered if she thought we'd eat eggs for lunch and dinner too.

"We have to get the pasta," I reminded her.

"There is time for that. The whore will have left for work by then."

I gathered that it would be okay to be in the other house when my grandmother and aunt were out.

"I don't know whether Pina is going to work today or not," I said.

"Don't talk to me about her."

After I'd had my second cup of coffee and egg of the morning, my mother unexpectedly began to cry quietly, and I suggested she return to bed. She seemed glad to go.

When my father arrived she was asleep. We sat at the kitchen table in our house, while I told him all that had happened, leaving out only what she'd said about his relationship with my grandmother and Pina. He paled and listened silently, but when I'd finished, he put his hand on my arm and told me he would take more time off and would try to help her get well.

In the days that followed, it seemed she would get well. She insisted on accompanying me to school as she always had, mumbling only slightly on the way. She got along well with the psychiatrist whom Dr. Gaione brought to the house, and she did not behave unusually toward Gaione himself. When the psychiatrist recommended a series of electric shock treatments, she submitted without argument to be accompanied to the hospital for them by my father. Four times he did so, taking the day off. When they'd return, my mother would look dazed and helpless, and go immediately to bed. On these days, I'd come home from school by myself. I had achieved a modicum of independence without fanfare or joy.

My mother still refused to go into the other house while my grandmother and Pina were home, but in the afternoon she did cook the evening meal there for everybody, and brought our portions to our side of the hall. She moderated her objections to my being in the other house with her mother and sister, after I pleaded with her that listening to the radio was important for keeping posted on the war and, hence, on Vinnie's future. First, she made me promise not to listen to the Italian radio station, and when I told her I had no intention of listening to it, she said, "Very well, take the cesspool with you to the other house, and do not bring it back."

THE HOMECOMING

My father's summer vacation began the Sunday after atomic bombs were dropped on Hiroshima and Nagasaki. We went to the ball game as usual, but on Monday we stayed home, listening to the radio in the other house, while my mother smoked in silence across the hall. I had previously told her of "the more powerful kind of dynamite" dropped on Japan, of Russia's declaration of war, and of the general feeling that peace was not far off. She'd seemed only barely interested.

On Tuesday, my father and I stayed home again by the radio, occasionally answering questions Uncle Charlie asked from his cot, and occasionally looking out of the front-room windows. All day, people on the street prepared to celebrate. Some milled around the Shrine of Our Lady of Mount Carmel, dropping in coins and lighting candles. Others walked down the middle of the street, from Third Avenue to Second Avenue and back again, waving at cars. A man in his undershirt consumed an entire case of beer before late afternoon in front of Denerstein's Iron Works.

I wished my mother could share the excitement. Every

hour or so, I'd run to our house to see her. I found her sitting at the kitchen table every time, smoking.

"Is it over yet?" she'd ask.

"Not yet. But it will be over today, everyone agrees. You should see what's going on outside."

"I won't believe it until I hear the bells. They will ring the bells of Camporeale when it ends."

When she came across the hall to start dinner, my father turned off the radio.

"Start tearing up newspapers," he told me. "When the time comes, we'll throw it out the window."

At six o'clock, we followed my mother to our side of the hall to eat. We were both impatient and left most of our food untouched, hurrying back to the other house, where my grandmother and Pina were still at their pasta. Charlie was getting ready to leave.

"You going to work tonight?" my father asked. "What the hell is the matter with you?"

"I ain't rich, that's what the hell's the matter with me," Charlie replied.

"But you're beautiful," my father said.

At seven we heard bells, not from Camporeale but from the radio, and then from all the churches in the neighborhood. In the street people cheered and screamed and my father and I began throwing out the torn newspaper. From windows up and down the block others were doing the same. The beer drinker in his undershirt danced in the blizzard. King George VI was talking on the radio as my grandmother and Pina came into the front room. Seeing what my father and I were doing, Pina ran to get a half-used roll of toilet paper from the *beckowzu*. She unfurled it into the street with a shriek. My grandmother sat down on one of the wooden kitchen chairs along the left wall, to say a rosary of thanksgiving. Between the mumbled decades, she remarked how "Churchillo the *ricuttaru* and Eleanora the frankfurter cook" had had their triumph.

"But Eleanora's loin-licking husband, The Green Rose, did not live to see it," she continued, more loudly. "He had finally caught on to what was going on between his wife and Churchillo. It happened coming back from the conference he and Churchillo had with Starlino. Don Nunzio told me all about it at *Li Roggispiti* today. The Green Rose confronted the Englishman on the airplane. 'No more will I lick your loins,' he said to him, 'for you have stolen my wife.' 'So now you know,' Churchillo said, 'so now you must die.' And he took out his sword and stabbed him again and again in the face and in the neck. He watched The Green Rose die at his feet."

My father and I stood dumbfounded.

"But," I finally said, "when Roosevelt came back from Yalta he rode around in an automobile and many people saw him. He made a speech to the Congress."

"You are too young to understand these things," my grandmother explained. "*Things there are, but we are not obliged to believe them.* They did not want to alarm the populace."

"But you saw his picture in the paper yourself. I showed it to you."

"It was a trick. A trick like when that man makes the wooden doll talk, the one you listen to, Charlie Macardu."

"That's ridiculous," my father said.

"Ridiculous? And what is more ridiculous than a head of state dying and his body not being shown to his people? Did you see his wife? Did she seem like a woman in mourning to you? She knew. Her boy friend, Churchillo, told her. She was glad to be rid of her husband so she could live with her illicit lover. Why do you think there is an armed guard around the grave all the time? It is so no one can go and open the coffin and prove it's empty, prove that his mutilated body was dumped from that airplane into the sea. There must be nothing left now. Generations of fish have already grown fat on The Green Rose."

She resumed mumbling Hail Marys as my father and I stared at each other for a long moment before bursting into laughter. We returned to the window and tossed out the rest of our newspaper.

"Boy, they must be going wild in Times Square," my father said. "This is nothing compared to what's going on there."

"Let's go there," I shouted. "Let's go, Pop."

"It'll be a madhouse. We'll get pushed around."

"So what? Let's go."

"Right. It'll be something to remember the rest of our lives."

"Where you going?" Pina asked, ducking her head inside from the other window.

"We're gonna give our regards to Broadway, Tommy and me."

"You'll get killed."

"It's a celebration," I said.

The tumult outside was growing louder as I dashed into our house, followed by my father.

"It's over," my mother smiled. "Now I believe it's over."

"Yes. And we're going to Broadway to celebrate."

She pulled out another cigarette from her pack. When my father bent to light it for her, she drew back uncertainly, but he held it until she inclined toward the flame. He burned himself but didn't wince.

We left without another word.

The Third Avenue El train going downtown was almost deserted, but everywhere we looked, people on the street were shouting, and those at home were throwing paper from windows. We got off at 42nd Street and began walking. At Fifth Avenue we started getting buffeted about. By the time we got past Sixth, our progress was no longer up to us. We were pushed to Times Square, where servicemen were kissing every woman they could get near, and women who weren't being kissed were screaming. A replica of the Statue of Liberty made of cardboard towered over us all. Drenched with sweat, my father and I, silent and smiling, held on to one another and submitted to the crowd.

Despite having been in the Army for nearly three years at V-J Day, my brother hadn't acquired enough "points" for immediate discharge, since he'd never been in combat. He didn't come home until January, on the day I started my last semester at Galvani.

For weeks I'd been pestering my mother to let me wear long pants. Finally, a few days before the start of the new term, she'd taken me to a store on First Avenue run by a Jewish man who spoke perfect Neapolitan dialect.

"You look best in blue," she said.

I nodded.

"Yes, mamma," the storekeeper said. "*Nu bello paio e causone blu pello guaglio?* A nice pair of blue pants for the boy?"

"Light blue," my mother specified. "Not dark like an old man. And not tight. They must fit comfortably."

She settled on a pair of woolly persian blue pants about five feet long. At home, she cut off a foot of material from the legs, turned them up, and told me to try them on before she cuffed them. They dragged on the floor, and I complained that they felt scratchy, but my mother was pleased.

"They are scratchy because they are of good material. They will keep you warm. You will look like a grown man when your brother comes home. He won't know you. It is our evil destiny that he should arrive on the day you start school. You should stay home to welcome him."

"I know," I said, pleased at how much she was talking. "But I can't stay home the first day."

Three days before my brother's homecoming, I began preparing for it. First I took separate sheets of my typewriter paper, and painted a different colored letter on each. I spread the finished work on the floor:

WELCOME HOME VINNIE

My mother studied the sheets.

"Seventeen pieces of paper? Why seventeen?"

"That's just the way it works out with the letters," I said.

"Couldn't you do something else? You know seventeen means disaster."

I tore up the last three sheets, and hung the balance on the wall between the other house and ours, over the coal sack. Then I began work on an eight-page, Special Edition of *The Daily Bugle*, made up of two more sheets of typewriter paper folded in half. My banner headline on Page One was: VINCENT MARTANA RETURNS HOME TODAY. TOP BASEBALL STARS REJOINING CLUBS. 1946 SEASON PROMISES TO BE GREATEST EVER. DAILY BUGLE BACK ON PEACETIME SCHEDULE.

I filled the paper with a resume of remembered high points of the preceeding three seasons and with more personal accounts of games I'd actually seen. I juxtaposed them with vignettes of what I imagined my brother had been doing at the time: "Vincent Martana Making Himself at Home in Japan; Brother Tommy and Father See Closing Game of 1945 Season."

On the big day, I awoke two hours earlier than usual. The cuffs on my new long pants were expertly made but still dragged on the floor.

"Let me go to school by myself today," I asked my mother. "Let's make it so that from now on I come and go by myself all the time, not just at noon."

"No," she said. "In the fall, when you get to the high school, all right, but for now, while I'm still able, I want to take you."

"But now that I have long pants, it will look funny for you to take me to school."

"Never mind about that. I'll take you this morning. You come home by yourself for lunch, and if your brother has already arrived you can take the rest of the day off, *veru?*"

"Sure," I said, "I'll tell the teacher about it. Let's get started now."

"Now? You still have over an hour. What are we going to do, stand for an hour in front of the school in the cold?"

So for an hour I rechecked *The Daily Bugle*, straightened the sign over the coal sack, and anticipated the great reunion with my brother, and the reaction of my classmates to my pants.

When I finally got to school, their response was friendly. Martinez advised me to walk carefully. He said the pants were long enough to sweep the floors. Tex agreed. I blushed, telling them that since I'd waited so many years for long pants, I'd decided to get pants as long as possible. They laughed politely.

Coming home at noon, Tex asked me how they felt. I told him they still felt funny.

"You'll get used to them. It's about time. What about your underwear? You still wearing those one-piece jobs with the flap and the buttons?"

I blushed again and told him I was wearing "regular" underwear—shorts and a T-shirt. I didn't say that the six pairs of boxer shorts my mother had bought me were almost big enough to fit my brother. The pair I was wearing was flopping around inside my scratchy pants.

"I guess your shirt ain't buttoned to your pants anymore either," Tex said. "Your pants are getting longer every minute. You better open your coat and tighten your belt. Maybe you should wear suspenders like that kid Acevedo. Maybe until you break 'em in, you should wear suspenders and a belt."

We both laughed. I felt a surge of elation and started to walk faster, in case Vinnie were already home.

He was. I found him sitting at the kitchen table in our house, eating a piece of Gorgonzola. My mother was standing quietly by the gas range. When she saw me come in, she lit the burner under the pot of Campbell's vegetable soup we would have for lunch. My brother rose to hug me. He was big and tanned and smelled good.

"That's some sign you made. Thanks."

"Wait," I said, running to get *The Daily Bugle* from the bureau in my bedroom—our bedroom it was again. He sat reading it and smiling while he finished the Gorgonzola and my mother poured soup into our three plates.

"Mom tells me Pop's coming home tonight," Vinnie said.

"That's right," I answered. "He says they're short a couple of waitresses this week and he has to go in. But he's coming home early tonight. He's been coming home a lot of nights lately anyhow."

"Really? How is he?"

"Fine."

"When did you start wearing long pants?"

"Today."

"They look pretty good." He repeated the compliment

in rusty Sicilian. My mother smiled and nodded, continuing to drink her soup.

"What's the matter with Mom? She's hardly said anything since I got here. When I asked about Grandma and Pina she didn't even answer."

At my brother's mention of the two names, my mother moved her lips in that old way of hers.

"Well, she got sick some time ago and started talking to herself," I said nervously. "She had to have shock treatments. She said not to write you about it so you wouldn't worry."

"What kind of treatments?"

"Electric shock."

"What's that?"

"I don't know how they work, exactly, but they were to get her back to reality and knock those strange ideas out of her head. I guess they did, but she was awfully quiet after. Actually, the last few weeks she's been doing a lot more talking."

"What strange ideas?"

"Oh, all kinds of things. She thought her female parent and her female sibling were trying to give her a fatal intake of nourishment. She still won't talk to them or go into the other house when they're there."

"*Who* was trying to do *what*?"

"You know. The people you asked about when she wouldn't answer you. I don't want to mention their names. It upsets her. Didn't you see her mouth just now when you mentioned their names?"

My brother looked blank.

"*Chi?*" my mother asked.

"*Nenti,*" I said. "Nothing."

"*E bellu lu Giappone?*" she asked Vinnie. "Is Japan beautiful?"

"There are a lot of people there," he answered. "But you, how do you feel? Tommy says you were sick. I *thought* something was wrong when you said we should eat on this side of the hall."

"The change of life," my mother said.

"So you feel better now, then?"

"After the change of life, one can only get worse."

"Don't talk that way. You're still young. Now that the war is over, you can forget those funny ideas."

"Don't speak of that now, my son," she said firmly. "You are still too innocent. But the tears of innocents are never shed in vain. Later I will tell you all that your mother has suffered."

After we finished the soup in silence, Vinnie asked my mother if I'd made my First Communion and Confirmation yet. She told him we'd been waiting for him to come home first.

Vinnie turned to me. "How old are you now, fourteen?"

"I'll be fourteen in April."

"You should have received the Sacraments long ago."

"Like Mom said, we were waiting for you."

"That's really no good reason. I mean, I appreciate it and everything, but you shouldn't have held it up just because I wasn't home. Suppose you were to die in this condition?"

214

I smiled weakly at my brother's unexpected, lugubrious concern for my immortal soul.

"Do you at least go to Mass on Sunday?"

I shook my head. "Mom doesn't go either, you know."

"I know. And look what happened. Maybe if she'd gone, she'd be okay now. Anyway, just because she doesn't go to Mass is no reason you can't go. You just came home from school by yourself."

"Just at noon. Mom still drops me off in the morning and picks me up at three o'clock. But she couldn't make four round-trips anymore."

"You could even go to Mass with Grandma. She still goes every week, doesn't she?"

"Yes," I said, glancing at my mother. Luckily, she seemed to have missed Vinnie's reference this time.

My brother rose from the table explaining haltingly in Sicilian the urgent need of my enrollment in a religious instruction class. I went into the *beckowzu* while my mother told him to make the necessary preparations, because she didn't know how to go about it. As I fumbled with the buttons on my scratchy fly, wondering at my brother's missionary zeal, I raised my hand automatically to the ledge, to feel the reassuring presence of the packet of pictures of my fisherwoman. They were gone. I should have remembered my brother was the one person in the family tall enough to look down at the ledge.

I stayed in *lu beckowzu* as long as I dared, red-faced and perspiring. When I finally emerged, my brother had his back to me, fumbling with the straps of an enormous duffle bag. I sat down, folding my left leg under me, while my mother began washing the dishes.

"I guess none of your old suits will fit any more," I said, hoping he wouldn't notice the quaver in my voice.

"I guess not," he answered, not turning around. "Shouldn't you start back to school now?"

"Well, I thought . . . yes, it's time."

"*Chi?*" asked my mother.

"It's time to go back to school."

"But we said this morning . . ."

"I'm going," I said, more loudly than was necessary. My mother sighed and told me to be careful.

THE VALEDICTORY

I prepared for my First Communion under the private tutelage of an elderly nun who was principal of Our Lady of Mount Carmel Parochial School. This special arrangement had been arrived at in the Sacristy of the church by my grandmother and the priest who gave her extra palms every Palm Sunday. He'd told her, my grandmother reported to my brother (at whose request she'd become involved) and me, that I was too old to attend the regular "release-time" children's classes and too young for the evening adult classes. My brother, who preferred to go to Mass at the "American" church of Our Lady Queen of Angels, thought the arrangement satisfactory. My mother, who was told nothing of my grandmother's role in the negotiations, wondered how I'd get to the church and back every Sunday at an hour when she had to prepare our main meal of the day. My father, not much interested in my spiritual welfare, nevertheless volunteered to take me.

From late February to early May, he and I attended the ten o'clock Mass at Our Lady of Mount Carmel. Even though the sermon at this Mass was in English, most of the congregation was made up of elderly women who moved with such difficulty that neither my father nor I ever learned when we should stand and when we should kneel. Most of them stayed for the Italian High Mass at eleven, the one my grandmother went to, while I went next door to the school for my half-hour with Sister Rosalie. In good weather, my father spent this time in Jefferson Park nearby, watching the old men of the neighborhood play bocci. In bad weather, he waited for me in one of the empty classrooms.

"It's not that you can't come and go by yourself," my father told me, "but we have to keep your mother happy."

"I know," I said. "It's funny how she lets me go to school most of the time now by myself, but she doesn't think I can make it to church and back alone."

"You've had almost three years to memorize the way to school, but you still might get lost on First Avenue," my father winked. "Mass isn't bad, though. Some of those sermons are interesting."

I'm not sure my brother would have approved of the way Sister Rosalie prepared me for my induction into the Army of Christ. She always spent the first couple of minutes looking over the top half of the front page of the New York *Times* which lay folded on her desk, while I looked over my Catechism. After motioning to me to draw my chair closer, she'd ask no more than four or five questions, taken verbatim from the Catechism, to which I always gave perfect answers. She'd compliment me and proceed to dismantle the *Times*, throwing the Magazine, Book Review, and everything else that slipped out, on the floor, and opening the main news section to its full length. As she turned its pages vigorously, slips of paper, pencils, paper clips, and rubber bands fell from her desk. I kept bending to pick them up. Some objects I caught in mid-air. She thanked me every time I retrieved one, continuing to turn pages and discuss current events.

"Do you know, Thomas, that the League of Nations only just now dissolved itself? It says here it turned over its assets to the UNO. My, my, I thought they'd gone out of business—thank you, Thomas—long ago. They certainly didn't do a very good job during the last few years, did they?"

"No, I guess not."

"Do you suppose the United Nations Organization will do any better?"

"I hope so."

"I hope so too, my boy—thank you, dear—but I doubt it. They've left God out of their little club. There's no mention of God in their charter, you know, and it is impossible to achieve peace without Jesus. They're just whistling in the dark."

Every time she mentioned Jesus, she gave a quick little nod of her head.

"I wonder if we'll ever truly have peace again. We're in for a great deal of strife, Thomas, both at home and overseas. Look at all these strikes. That's all this paper is filled with—thank you, Thomas—strike, strike, strike. Ah, well, we're fighting among ourselves here and soon we'll be fighting the communists over there. God must be mightily displeased. War crimes—these war crimes they keep talking about, Thomas. How can you put a few people on trial for war crimes when war itself—thank you, dear—the act of war itself is a crime?"

At our last meeting, Sister Rosalie put her brown-flecked hand on my arm and told me that "Father" would examine me on Wednesday afternoon in the Sacristy to see if I were ready for the Sacraments.

"Father is a good man, you needn't be afraid of him. He looks like Primo Carnera, but he has a kind heart. And you've learned your lessons well."

"Father" turned out to be a priest I'd never seen at Mass and a rough-looking customer indeed. He wasn't nearly as tall as Carnera, but he did have a broken nose and cauliflower ears. He also needed a shave. Despite Sister Rosalie's assurance, his appearance flustered me so much that, early in the interview, I misinterpreted the Doctrine of the Immaculate Conception. In response to his question, I described it as "Jesus being born of a Virgin."

"No, son," he said. "Dat ain't right. Dat's the commonest mistake dat's made about our fait. It ain't got nuttin to do with Jesus, d'Immaculate Conception."

Like Sister Rosalie, he inclined his head when he mentioned the Holy Name.

"I'm sorry, Father. I meant it refers to Mary being born without the stain of Original Sin," I said.

"Correct, son. D'udder ting is de Voigin Boit, right?" He gave me a playful poke on the chin with his closed fist that jolted my head back.

"You'll be a good Cat'lic. But don't tink dat you make

your Communion an Confummation an dat'll be de end of it. It'll be just de beginnin of your Cat'lic life."

I was brought to this threshold the following Saturday afternoon by my brother, who led me to the door of the confessional. Inside, I renounced the accumulated sins of fourteen years. The next day Vinnie took me to the altar rail for my First Communion, which I had trouble swallowing, and the following Sunday he took me inside the rail, in his capacity as sponsor at my Confirmation. My mother and father were both present at the two ceremonies, but there were no parties afterwards and no gifts except money: ten dollars from my father, five apiece from my mother and Vinnie. My grandmother gave me five too, out of my mother's sight. I was glad to get it over with. Even as I was being anointed by the Bishop in Confirmation, I'd been thinking a month ahead, to my graduation from Galvani, at which I'd be making the valedictory address.

At the time Mrs. Schmidt, my home room teacher in 9B-1, had broken the news to me, I'd never heard the word "valedictorian."

"It means you'll be making the farewell speech," she explained.

I blushed and shook my head.

"What's the matter?" asked Mrs. Schmidt.

"I can't make a speech."

"Why can't you?"

"Somebody else could probably do it better."

"Only one student can be the valedictorian, Thomas,

221

the one who's compiled the best scholastic record during the past three years. That's you."

Me? I'd never volunteered information; my record in Physical Education was non-existent; during the last year, I'd cut many classes with Zircon Roon; I'd done everything possible to hold my I.Q. in check. How could it be? Just the exams?

"Enrique Rodriguez has the second best record," Mrs. Schmidt went on. "He'll be the salutatorian. It's a great honor for you both, Thomas."

"I know, but couldn't they just read our names or something?"

"Mr. Abramowitz of the English Department will help you with your speeches. I'm sure you'll do fine. You're both very bright students."

When I told her what was going to happen, my mother said only that I should do what I was told and not worry. My brother was equally unhelpful.

"So you're the smartest kid in the school? What's your average?" he asked.

"My teacher told me it's ninety-two, point five."

"That's all? That's pretty low to be highest in the school."

"I guess it's not a very smart school. This kid Rodriguez who's second, only has an eighty-five average."

"Boy. At West Side I was ahead of you both and I was about ninth in my class."

I was sure my father would be appropriately enthusiastic at the honor in store for me. But at the ball game that Sunday, I decided not to say anything about it. It would be fun to surprise him. I knew my mother and brother wouldn't spoil the surprise, judging from their reactions.

Mr. Abramowitz helped me write my speech. The first time I practiced it aloud, I stumbled over practically every other word.

Mr. Abramowitz decided to get tough about it. "Listen, Martana. I've known you since you were in my freshman English class. I know what you can do. I know that there are damn few kids that have your kind of brain. But the way you've goofed it up these three years is inexcusable. You made it as valedictorian, but you don't fool me. I know you've just coasted through Galvani on one cylinder. Now, I don't know why you don't live up to your potential. I don't know why a kid who's got all your talent is all screwed up. That's your business. But this speech is *my* business too, and you're not going to screw this up. You're going to do it as well as you can. And that's damned good. Remember that when you're up there. Remember that you're smarter than anybody else in the whole goddamn place. You're smarter than me, even. So what in the hell are you afraid of?"

My classmates and I were still inscribing one another's autograph books as we filed into the auditorium for our commencement exercises on the morning of Friday, June 28, 1946. To the piano accompaniment of Miss Redfield, a teacher of Music Appreciation, Zircon Roon wrote a meaningless jingle in mine, which didn't even rhyme. "To Martin, Don't make love by the garden gate. Love is blind but the neighbors ain't. Your friend, Tex."

We stood to pledge allegiance to the flag. We continued

to stand as our principal, Mr. Baldner, read the First Psalm, followed by our singing of "Oh, Worship the King." All of us except Enrique Rodriguez then sat down. Rodriguez strode rapidly to the stage, where he stuttered through his salutation. He strode even more rapidly back to his seat while the audience applauded and our class rose again to sing "The Lord Is My Shepherd." After that, we recited the Junior High School Code of Behavior in perfect unison. The weeks of home room practice had really paid off. The Galvani Glee Club then performed on stage two works described in our programs as: "(a) Ching-a-Ling Anonymous," and "(b) The Donkey Serenade Friml." Next, a Negro identified as the Reverend Claude Oliver Hooper made his address to the graduates. At its conclusion, we sang "The Ship of State." Finally came the awarding of prizes and certificates. By pre-arrangement, the Certificate for Excellence in English was presented last. So when I walked up to accept it from Mr. Baldner, I did not have to return to my seat. I just turned around to the lectern and intoned by rote my valedictory address.

Later, Vinnie told me I'd gone through it beautifully, without a hitch. He was the only member of my family in the audience. Two nights before my graduation, my brother and I had been awakened by my mother. She was banging a kitchen chair on the floor and screaming, "They are not going to kill my two sons in their bed." Before we could calm her, she had broken all four legs off the chair. Pina had gone downstairs to use The Elephant's phone to call an ambulance, and an hour later, Vinnie and I accompanied my mother to the psychiatric ward of Bellevue Hospital. We didn't call my father to tell him. Three days earlier he had fallen across a customer's roast beef in Kreiner's restaurant, the victim of a heart attack.

THE ROOM

We didn't tell my father of my mother's disastrous relapse until after he'd been discharged from the hospital and was convalescing in his room in Newark. She was home by then. After two weeks in Bellevue, the doctors had told Vinnie there was nothing more to be done for her there. It was up to the family to decide, they said, whether they wanted her home or in a state institution, but they couldn't keep her in Bellevue. One of them wrote out a prescription and wished us luck.

On our weekend visits to East Orange General Hospital, Vinnie and I had attributed my mother's absence to a newly developed fear of underground travel which prevented her from accompanying us on the Hudson Tube. We always took him her best regards. The truth was she never mentioned him. She seemed not to remember that he'd suffered a heart attack. Neither did she remember that I'd been scheduled to graduate. In fact, she appeared to remember nothing of the events preceeding her admission to Bellevue, not even the imagined plotting of my grandmother and Pina. My grandmother had retired from Rogers

Peet to stay home and prepare our meals. When Vinnie or I took my mother's portions to her, she accepted them without questioning their source. A couple of times my grandmother, beginning to hope for a reconciliation or, at least, a reaction, had taken them in personally. My mother hadn't raised an eyebrow. She stayed on our side of the hall all day, just sitting in the kitchen. She took no part in conversation, and the only question she ever answered was the one I asked her two or three times a day, "What's the matter?" "Nothing," she always replied softly, never looking up from her hands.

My father's room in Newark was about the size of our kitchen. There were two windows with drapes and venetian blinds, raised to let in sunlight and a view of a park across the street. There was a square green rug on the floor, not quite wall-to-wall. The ceiling fixture, shaped like half a globe, leaned to one side. There weren't many furnishings —a bed, an easy chair, a wicker chair, a low coffee table, and a bureau. On the bureau were a radio and the old pictures of Vinnie and me my grandmother had found in the trunk, as well as a more recent one of Vinnie in uniform. There were two closets, both with doors ajar. Through a more widely opened door, I could see the bathroom. It looked very much like the one in which I'd watched my father shave.

"How do you like it?" he asked, welcoming us. "First time you've seen it, isn't it?"

He was wearing a dark-blue robe over light-blue pajamas. His normal ruddy color, drained during his hospital stay, seemed on its way back. He'd put on weight, too.

"We need another chair. Mister Kreiner has plenty of chairs. His apartment is right next door. He owns this building you know. I doubt he's home, but I've got the key."

My brother and I stood stiffly awaiting my father's return.

He came bustling back holding aloft a metal folding chair. Vinnie and I both moved to help him, but he vigorously snapped it open himself.

"Mister Kreiner's home, but he's taking a bath," he said. "He'll be over later. He wants to meet you both. Sit down, sit down. Did you have any trouble with the bus?"

"No, it was right there waiting when we got out of the Tube," I said. I extended a box of chocolates. "Here, we brought you this."

"Oh, boy! Barricini. You know, since I stopped smoking I can't get enough of this stuff. I'm getting a pot like Babe Ruth. Sit down, boys. Thank you for the candy."

I sat on the folding chair, Vinnie sat on the wicker one, and my father went to the easy chair, picking at his gift.

"Very good. You want some?" he asked, offering the box to each of us in turn. We declined, and he set it on the coffee table.

"Well. How's your mother?"

"She's okay," Vinnie answered quickly.

"Why don't you tell me what's really wrong," my father said. "You afraid I'll have another heart attack?"

My brother protested blushingly that everything really *was* okay.

"At least she's out of the hospital," I said.

My brother gave me an accusing look.

"Don't you remember how mad you were that we didn't write to you about Grandpa?" I reminded him. "And when Mom didn't mention anything about my heart to Pop, he was mad too." I was astonished at my candor in my father's presence.

"I *thought* she was probably in the hospital," my father said. "What was it, her cough? Something wrong with her lungs?"

"No. It was the other thing again. She thought somebody was trying to kill Vinnie and me, so she started busting up the furniture in the kitchen. We had to take her to Bellevue."

"Is she any better?"

"Much better," Vinnie assured him, but once more I contradicted him.

"She's not ranting and raving and breaking chairs, but you can't say she's better. They told us at Bellevue she'll never really get better, and she could get wild again any time. They left it up to us whether to put her someplace permanent or keep her home."

"What does she do all day?"

"Nothing. She doesn't even smoke much anymore. She hardly seems to know who we are. She's got pills, but I don't know whether she takes them."

My father was silent for a long time. A piece of chocolate he'd picked up absent-mindedly was melting between his fingers. When at last he noticed it, he put it into his mouth

229

and went to the bathroom to wash his hands. He emerged asking after my grandmother.

"She's okay," Vinnie said. "She stays home now to cook and clean. Naturally, she's a little upset."

"About your mother or about having to stay home?"

"Both, I guess," Vinnie answered lamely.

"And Pina?" My father settled into his easy chair again.

"She's okay too. She's got a new job in Bloomingdale's."

"That's nice. At least there's still money coming in there." Vinnie nodded.

"And Uncle Charlie? Still living in the other house?" I answered this time. "Yeah, but he keeps talking about going back to Sicily."

"I hope he finds his way there better than he found his way to East Orange. None of them came to see me once. I hope it was because they were all tired from going to visit your mother every day. Did they?"

I shook my head. "Grandma and Pina would have gone, but you know how she felt about them."

"Yes," he answered, turning his head away. Though he hid his face from us, there was no way he could hide the sobs that were suddenly wracking his body. When he turned to face us again, his eyes, his nose, his forehead, and his chin were all dripping. I reached into my back pocket for one of the two handkerchiefs I always carried and handed him the clean one.

"And your uncle Nick and the family?" he asked, sniffling.

"They're all right, I guess. We haven't seen them lately."

There was a tap at the door, and my father, giving his

face another hasty wipe and stuffing the handkerchief into
the breast pocket of his robe, went to open it. His face
brightened as he showed his boss in.

"Hello, Oscar. These are my two sons, Vinnie and
Tommy," he said. Mr. Kreiner shook hands with us firmly,
saying he was glad to meet us because he'd heard a lot of
good things about us. He was a tall gray-haired man with
a deeply furrowed brow, wearing a light suit and a bright,
flowery necktie.

"Your father looks very well, don't you think?"

I motioned for Mr. Kreiner to take my chair.

"No, no, that's all right, Tommy. I can only stay a minute.
I just wanted to meet you boys. I understand you spent
three years in the Army, Vinnie."

"Yes sir, that's right."

"And you, Tommy, you just graduated from, was it
high school?"

"No, junior high."

"Good. Your dad's very proud of you, you know. And
how's your mother?"

My father answered that she'd been ill, but was better.

"Uh-huh. Well, you boys tell her for me that I'd very
much like to meet her sometime. Tell her her husband's
quite a man." Mr. Kreiner turned to my father jovially.
"And how are you feeling this fine day, Mario me boy?
Think you can come back to work this afternoon?"

"I'm never coming back if you wear ties like that in
the place," my father joked. "I haven't seen a tie like that
since Pete Pizzi."

"And who, pray tell, is Pete Pizzi?"

"My best man. He came up from New Orleans for the wedding and stayed in New York for three years. We even worked together for a while in a German restaurant. My wife told me once he brought me home one night when I'd had too much to drink and he helped put me to bed. Then, even though she kept telling him 'Good night,' he was hanging around, hemming and hawing and not leaving. Finally he said, 'Excuse me, *cummare*, but the best remedy is to apply hot olive oil to his balls,' and he ran out the door."

We all laughed loudly. My father was back in story-telling form. I hoped he wasn't overtiring himself.

"That's one hell of a hangover remedy, Mario. I'm glad he wasn't my best man," Mr. Kreiner said. "So what about the loud ties this guy wore?"

"The place we worked in New Orleans, that's where I met him. It was a speakeasy run by three brothers named Rossati. They had red, white, and green tablecloths and napkins, like the Italian flag. Anyhow, Pete liked them so much he stole a tablecloth and cut it up to make neckties."

"Don't let me catch you wearing any of *my* tablecloths, Mario."

"Oh, sure, that's just what I want—a white necktie that says 'Standard Linen Supply' on it."

Mr. Kreiner laughed so hard he had to wipe his eyes. "What did the boss do when he saw this guy's neckties?" he said finally.

"Rossati? He just laughed. Enzo, that was. The other brothers were almost never there. But Enzo didn't care what you stole. You know, the night I went to tell him I had to go to New York to get married, I remember I was carrying the receipts. He was very upset. He said to me that I had a good future with him. He said I was too young to get married. And anyhow, he said, that wasn't the way people got married in America. See, my mother wrote me from the old country that the marriage had been all arranged between my father and my wife's father. The old man was going back and forth between New York and Camporeale in those days. Anyhow, my mother wrote, 'Go to New York and marry the daughter of Gaetano Tarantola.' I didn't even know my future wife, but that was it. I told Rossati I didn't want to disappoint nobody. He sort of shrugged and told me he'd leave the room while I counted the receipts. I said, 'What do you mean, Mister Rossati, I already counted it. There's nine hundred and forty-three dollars.' Then he said to me, 'Mario, you mean to tell me that all this time you been handling all this money and you haven't been putting a few bucks in your pocket every night?' I was surprised as hell. He shook his head and told me that if he'd been in my place he would have robbed his own brothers. He told me I should have been rich. He almost started to cry. Then he said to take what I wanted from the receipts as a wedding present. I took two hundred."

Mr. Kreiner shook his head slowly. "How long ago was that, Mario?"

"Almost twenty-eight years. We were married twenty-seven years ago yesterday."

Neither my brother nor I had remembered.

"My God," Mr. Kreiner said. "Why didn't you tell me? Why didn't you boys come yesterday and bring your mother?"

"She's not up to the trip yet," my father answered.

"Well, no ginny bootlegger is outdoing Oscar Kreiner," my father's boss said. He took out his checkbook and wrote a check for three hundred dollars. "Happy anniversary," he said.

My father blurted his surprised thanks. My brother got so nervous he lit a cigarette. He exhaled quickly, looking guiltily at my father.

"That's all right, Vinnie, it doesn't bother me," my father said. He ostentatiously stuffed two chocolates into his mouth and Mr. Kreiner and I laughed.

"Say, Vinnie," Mr. Kreiner said. "Have you got a job yet?"

"No, sir."

"Do you plan to go back to school under the G. I. Bill?"

"No, I don't think so."

"Well, if it should interest you, I can use a bookkeeper at the place. I think my brother ought to retire. I think that sonofabitch is really Enzo Rossati and he's robbing me blind."

My brother flushed in embarrassment and grunted noncommittally.

"How are you at arithmetic?"

"Okay, I guess."

"Well, you're bound to be better than my brother. Think it over. It was very nice meeting you boys. Take good care of your father."

He shook hands with us again, and gave my father a friendly pat on the stomach. "What do you want me to send up from the kitchen tonight? You know how lousy the Sunday menu is better than I do."

"London broil, I guess—but with all the money I have, I really ought to pay for it."

"You can buy me a new necktie sometime. Shall I send up something for the boys, too? Are they staying?"

"I guess not," Vinnie said. "Thanks a lot, though."

"Okay, good-by, boys."

"He's a nice guy," my father said.

Vinnie nodded.

"It wouldn't be so bad working for him. He'd give you a good salary."

"Well, nah . . ."

"You don't want it?"

"It's just I'm so used to New York now. And with Mom sick, I ought to stay close . . . you know."

"I guess you're right. Besides, there's no hurry. You still got the twenty dollars a week coming in from the government."

Vinnie shifted uneasily in his chair as my father reached for another chocolate.

"Do you remember this part of Newark at all, Tommy?"

"No," I said. "I was never downtown when we lived here."

"No? I guess I never took you. Vinnie was around here plenty, though. Right, Vinnie? You used to come downtown to the movies."

"That's right. It's changed a lot."

After nearly an hour of strained reminiscences about Newark, my father, deferring to Vinnie's fidgetiness, said, "Well, I guess you boys have to go."

Vinnie rose, much relieved. I rose too, to go to the bathroom. It wasn't quite like the one I remembered. It was slightly smaller, the bathtub wasn't as long, and the tiles on the floor were large squares instead of little hexagons. But there was the same clean smell of shaving cream.

"Do we really have to go now?" I asked my brother when I came out.

"Well, we have to go eat, and I'm going to the Novena tonight. You want to come?"

"What's wrong?" my father asked me.

"Nothing. It's just, well, I thought we could listen to the second game of the doubleheader."

"Jesus, I forgot all about the game." He got up and switched on the radio.

I smiled and sat down again. Vinnie was still standing by the door.

"I tell you what, Vinnie," my father said. "Tommy could sleep here tonight. Mister Kreiner has all kinds of cots and extra beds in the basement. And tomorrow he can drive him to New York. He always goes."

Vinnie seemed undecided for a moment before saying, "Okay."

"Give my love to your mother," my father said. "And don't worry. Here, wait a minute."

He went to the bureau, took a pen from the top drawer, and endorsed the check Mr. Kreiner had made out. He handed it to Vinnie.

"See if she wants it. Tell her it's an anniversary present. Maybe she'll remember."

When my brother left, I got up from the folding chair and stretched out on my father's bed to listen to the game, wondering what London broil tasted like.